A Reader's Digest Songbook

Editor: William L. Simon
Music arranged and edited by Dan Fox
Project Editor: Mary Kelleher
Associate Editor: Natalie Moreda
Designer: Karen Mastropietro
Music Associate: Elizabeth Mead

Annotated by Richard M. Sudhalter
and Clair Van Ausdall

READER'S DIGEST GENERAL BOOKS
Editor in Chief: John A. Pope, Jr.; *Managing Editor:*
Jane Polley; *Art Director:* David Trooper;
Group Editors: Norman B. Mack; Joel Musler *(Art)*,
Susan J. Wernert; *Chief of Research:* Monica
Borrowman; *Copy Chief:* Edward W. Atkinson; *Picture
Editor:* Robert J. Woodward; *Rights and Permissions:*
Dorothy M. Harris; *Head Librarian:* Jo Manning

THE READER'S DIGEST ASSOCIATION, INC.
Pleasantville, New York/Montreal

ISBN 0-89577-274-4

Printed in the United States of America

Introduction

*D*id you see Ordinary People, the 1980 Academy Award-winning movie about the trials and tribulations of a well-to-do Midwestern family? And did you, like so many other people, leave the theater humming the film's haunting background melody—a melody that you later heard in numerous recordings and television commercials? Well, the music that seemed so fitting for that tale of contemporary American life is a 300-year-old liturgical canon by a German composer named Johann Pachelbel.

And do you recall the theme used in the film Kramer vs. Kramer? Again, centuries-old music, this time a mandolin concerto written in the early 1700s by the Venetian composer Antonio Vivaldi.

These are just two examples of what we mean by "popular classics," melodies that are, almost literally, in the air that we breathe—the sultry rhythms of Rimsky-Korsakov's Scheherazade or "Anitra's Dance" from Grieg's Peer Gynt, portions of Tchaikovsky's The Nutcracker and Bizet's Carmen. We hear such pieces played in concert halls and opera houses; we listen to them in films, on radio and television, and, of course, on records, tapes and compact discs. They are melodies whose inspired beauty and vitality have not and will not diminish with the passing of years. We hear them and we respond. It's as simple as that, and that is arguably the key to all great music.

For this book, we have combed the musical landscape to bring you more than 90 of the most beautiful and beloved popular classics. We've selected melodies from many musical areas, from many parts of the world and from several centuries. There are unforgettable themes—some, like Pachelbel's Canon, quite old; some, like the "Indiana Jones March," quite new—that we've come to recognize from TV and films. There are selections excerpted from immortal symphonies and concertos by such great composers as Mozart, Beethoven, Mendelssohn and Brahms. And there are glorious melodies from operas by Verdi, Puccini and Rossini; spirited waltzes by Johann Strauss, Jr.; as well as lilting pieces based on traditional Hungarian, Slavonic and Spanish dances. But we've also looked to this side of the Atlantic and more recent times. You'll find marches by John Philip

Sousa (one of them will sound familiar to you from the Monty Python show) and blues by George Gershwin and Duke Ellington.

We've also put in a few surprises. You'll be delighted by a modern jewel in an ancient dance form, "American Minuet" by Harold Arlen, the great pop songwriter. And we've included a brand-new piece that we think should become a classic: "One-Note Rag" by Dan Fox, who has arranged all the selections in Popular Classics as well as those in the 11 other Reader's Digest music books.

In this book, as in our previous classical-music book, Great Music's Greatest Hits, music that might have been written for a symphony or chamber orchestra has been adapted for the piano (and for the organ as well) in arrangements that retain the flavor and strength of the originals yet lie within reach of anyone with basic keyboard ability. These made-for-you miniatures of the world's masterpieces, far superior to the "classics made easy" remembered from childhood piano lessons, do full justice to the genius of the great composers.

The adaptations let you play classical melodies as easily as you can play popular tunes. Chord symbols have been indicated above the staves so that, if your home-style piano playing is based on chord symbols for the left hand, you can use them to create your own arrangements of the music we've selected. And, as with all of our music books, technically speaking, Popular Classics has something for everyone. Many of the arrangements are easy, a few are fairly difficult. The organ-pedal notes—those small notes found in the left-hand staves throughout—need not be played on the piano, although if your technique will allow it, they make a nice addition to the richness of the left hand.

Enough words. Better for every reader to turn now to our first selection, the enchanting "Mi chiamano Mimi" from La Bohème, and discover what was so well described more than a century ago by the great musician, poet and statesman E.T.A. Hoffmann: "an unknown region, a world that has nothing in common with the world that surrounds us, a world in which we leave behind all ordinary feelings to surrender ourselves to an inexpressible longing." In this case, discover the world of Popular Classics.

Reader's Digest has published 11 other music books: *Family Songbook, Treasury of Best Loved Songs, Family Songbook of Faith and Joy, Festival of Popular Songs, Great Music's Greatest Hits, The Merry Christmas Songbook, Popular Songs That Will Live Forever, Country and Western Songbook, Unforgettable Musical Memories, Children's Songbook* and *Remembering Yesterday's Hits.*
(A few songs appear in more than one book,
but the musical arrangements are always different.)
You can order the books from Reader's Digest, Pleasantville, New York 10570.

ART CREDITS: **Cover:** *Yvonne and Christine Lerolle at the Piano* by Pierre Auguste Renoir (Giraudon/Art Resource). **Ray Lago:** pages 10, 16, 18, 22, 23, 30, 34, 40, 41, 44, 46, 76, 77, 78, 89, 91, 104, 148, 160, 228.
Bob McMahon: pages 8, 24, 28, 37, 50, 57, 68, 72, 74, 84, 94, 100, 102, 114, 122, 138, 140, 144, 158, 159, 166, 168, 170, 174, 176, 194, 196, 197, 206, 212, 213, 214, 215, 216, 217, 220, 221, 222, 232, 240, 244.
Jerry Pinkney: pages 92, 93. **Glenn Tunstull:** pages 48, 69, 71, 97, 110, 155, 225. **Pat Zadnick:** page 7.

Reader's Digest Fund for the Blind is publisher of the Large-Type Edition of *Reader's Digest.* For subscription information about this magazine, please contact Reader's Digest Fund for the Blind, Inc., Dept. 250, Pleasantville, N.Y. 10570.

Index to Sections

Index to Selections

1
Popular Melodies from Great Operas

Mi chiamano Mimi

from **La Bohème**   Giacomo Puccini

In Puccini's La Bohème, *Rodolfo is a poet who lives in a Parisian garret, poor but happy, not yet successful but still young. It is Christmas Eve, and, to provide a bit of warmth for himself and his equally penniless friends, he sacrifices his latest masterpiece, stuffing the pages of his poem into the fire. Shortly after his companions leave, he hears a timid knock at the door. It is the little seamstress from downstairs, as poor as Rodolfo and very frail. Frail, yes, but beautiful. When the girl drops her door key, Rodolfo helps search for it on the floor. Their hands meet, hers desperately cold. That touch is all that is needed. In a moment he is telling her the story of his life, and she responds with hers. "Mi chiamano*

Mimi" ("They call me Mimi"), she says, though her name is really Lucia. She embroiders silks and linens for a meager living; she is a good girl, modest, unpretentious and religious. Puccini's genius for transcribing patterns of the speaking voice into musical lines is nowhere more apparent than in this aria. In only a measure or two, he creates for his audience a portrait of a lovely, living, fascinating character. Rodolfo falls hopelessly in love with Mimi and remains so throughout the opera, until she finally perishes from consumption (tuberculosis). The disease was common in early-19th-century France, the setting for Henri Murger's Scènes de la Vie de Bohème, *the basis of the opera.*

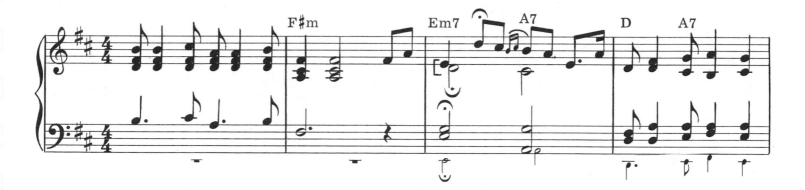

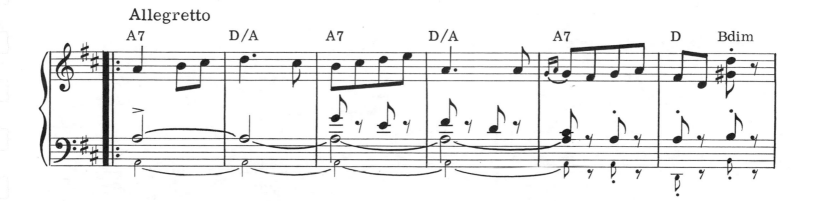

5

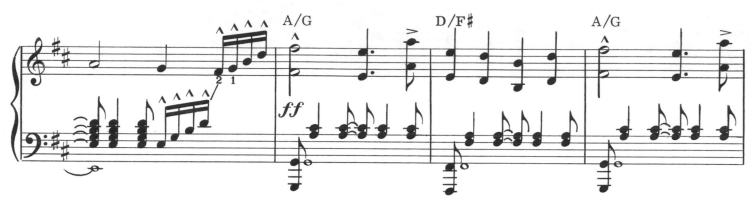

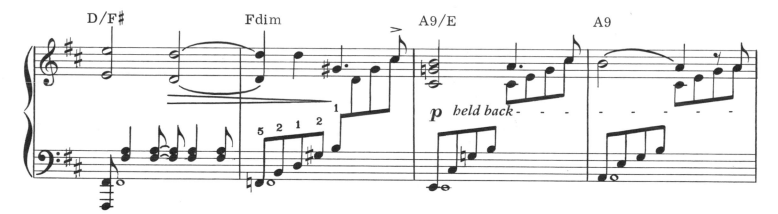

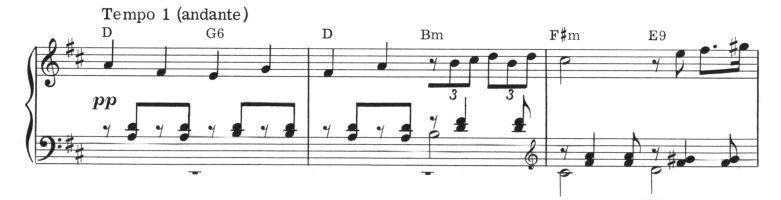

O mio babbino caro

from **Gianni Schicchi** Giacomo Puccini

The one-act opera Gianni Schicchi is Puccini's only comic work. His inspiration for it reached back to the magnificent city of Florence in the year 1299. A rich man has died, and his relatives are furious and scandalized to find that he has left his fortune to the Church rather than to them. One of them sends for the wily Gianni Schicchi, who takes the dead man's place in bed and, imitating his voice, declares that he is still alive and intends to make a new will. He promptly dictates the will to the hastily assembled notary and witnesses. Naturally, he fobs off the relatives with small inheri-

tances and gives himself — as the longtime friend of the deceased — the main treasures. Schicchi intends the inheritance for his own daughter, Lauretta, who is in love with Rinuccio, a relative of the dead man. The money will make it possible for them to marry. Lauretta has already persuaded her father to help her in the lovely but all-too-brief "O mio babbino caro" ("O, my beloved Daddy"). It is the opera's only true aria and one of Puccini's loveliest, the magnificent principal melody, with its soaring octave jump upward, set off by the poignant phrase in the final three measures.

Flowing

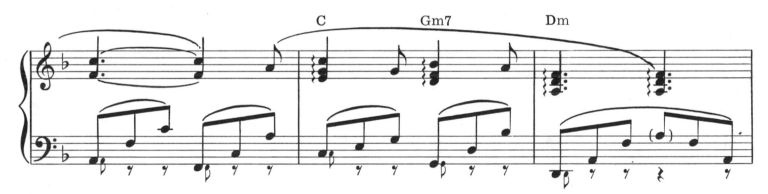

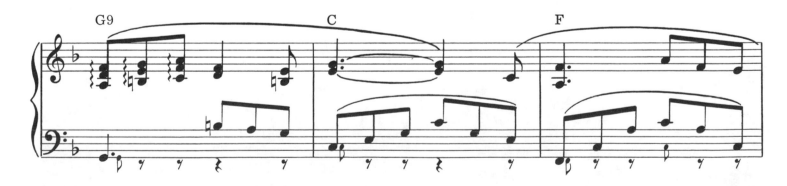

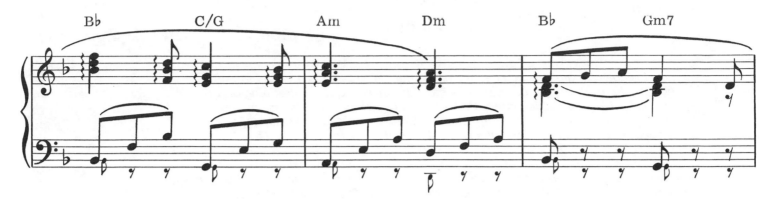

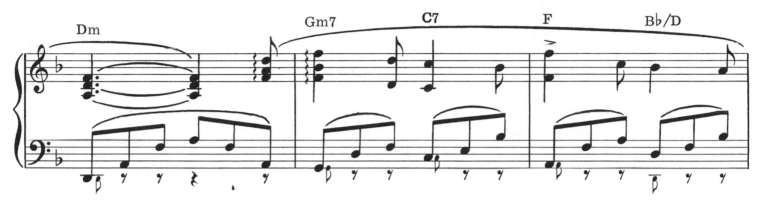

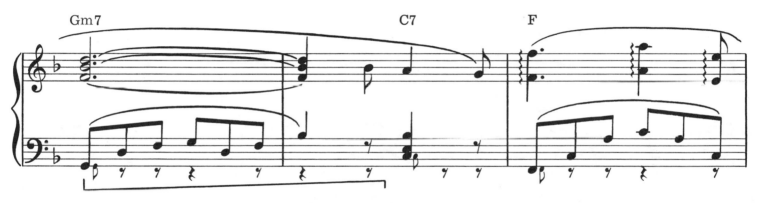

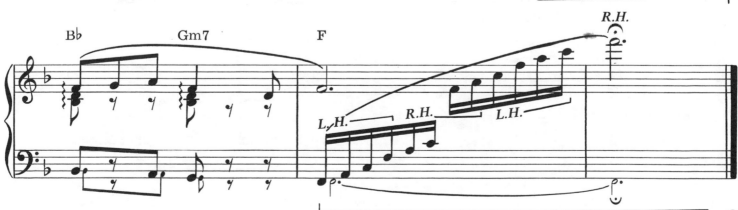

Un bel dí
(One Fine Day)

from **Madame Butterfly**
Giacomo Puccini

In Madame Butterfly, an American naval lieutenant stationed in Nagasaki marries a young Japanese girl in a Japanese civil ceremony. The wedding alienates his bride from her family, who are furious that she has renounced her ancestral religion and who probably realize that Lieutenant Pinkerton will leave her and Japan when his orders change. That is exactly what happens. Cio-Cio-San, or Madame Butterfly as Pinkerton nicknames her because of her gracefully fluttering walk, is still deliriously in love when the officer is transferred back to the United States. He promises to return. Butterfly believes him and, with just her maidservant, sets about making a solitary life for herself and her small son by Pinkerton. When the servant voices doubts that the master will return, Butterfly rebukes her and then sings the achingly beautiful "Un bel dí" ("One Fine Day"). Three years later, Pinkerton's ship returns. Butterfly waits for him as the sun sets and night falls, but he does not come. When he does arrive the next morning, it is with an American woman he has married. They are there to take the child away. Before he started to work on Madame Butterfly, Puccini listened to hundreds of Oriental songs, most of them Japanese. As a result, "Un bel dí," like so many of the other melodies in the opera, is based on the Oriental pentatonic, or five-note, scale, such as we hear when we play only the black notes on the piano.

Very slowly and calmly

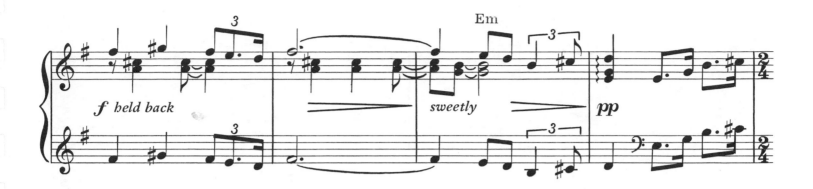

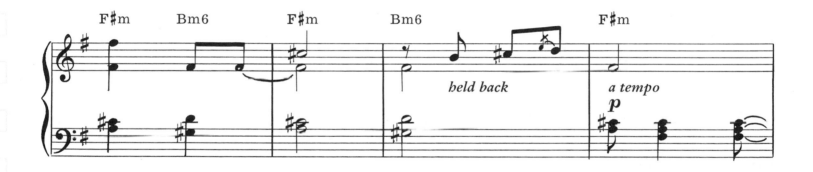

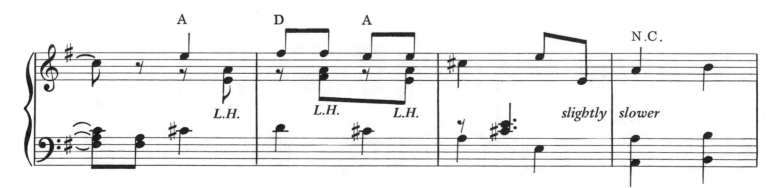

First tempo

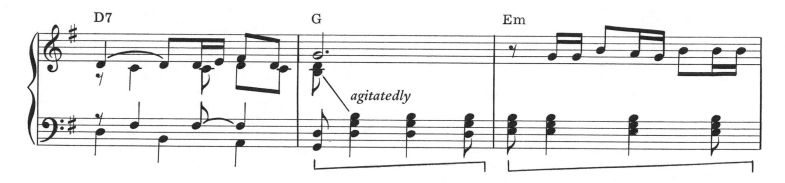

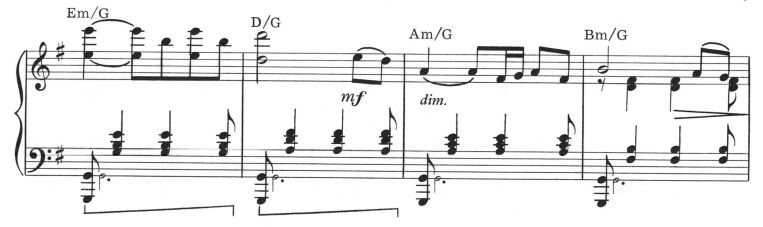

Mignon Gavotte

Ambroise Thomas

Mignon, *written by French composer Ambroise Thomas in 1866, is based on the famous novel* Wilhelm Meister *by Johann Wolfgang von Goethe. (That essentially Germanic tale, however, is turned completely Gallic in the libretto that Thomas chose, and the emphasis, obviously, is on Mignon, one of the novel's female characters, rather than on Wilhelm.) Mignon is a mysterious girl about whose background and parentage nothing is known. She has been brought up by Gypsies, who treat her miserably. When the handsome young student Wilhelm first spies her, she has refused to dance for some onlookers and is about to be beaten. Wilhelm rescues her, buys her freedom and makes her his page, dressing her in boys' clothing to conceal the*

fact that she is a woman. Meanwhile, his heart has succumbed to the beautiful actress Philene, and the rivalry between the two women for his affections becomes the centerpiece of the opera. Thomas placed this beautiful Gavotte at the close of Act I. (A gavotte is a type of dance that reached the height of its popularity 200 years earlier at the court of Louis XIV, the Sun King.) Mignon was Thomas's biggest success. In 1871, he became head of the Paris Conservatory and lacked the time to compose any more significant music. But a grateful France continued to remember him, and in 1894, on the occasion of the 1,000th performance of the opera, he was awarded the Grand Cross of the Legion of Honor, the first composer to be so honored.

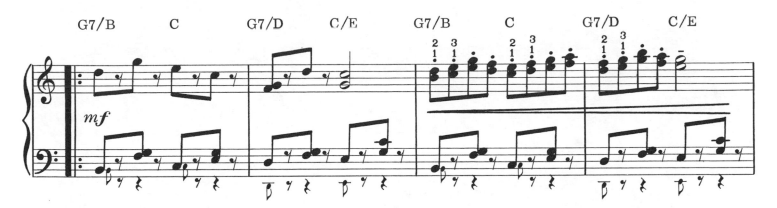

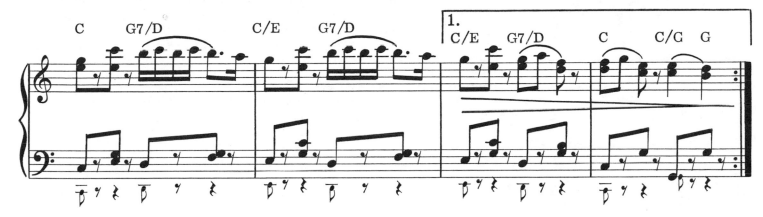

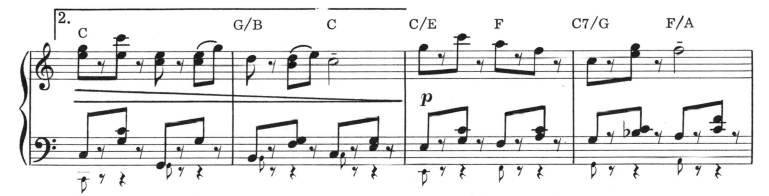

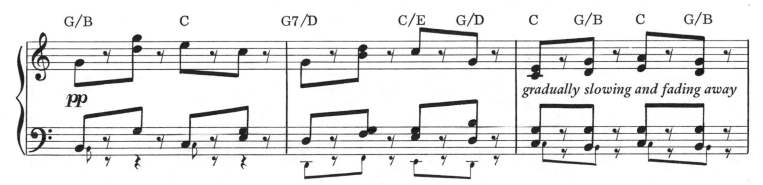

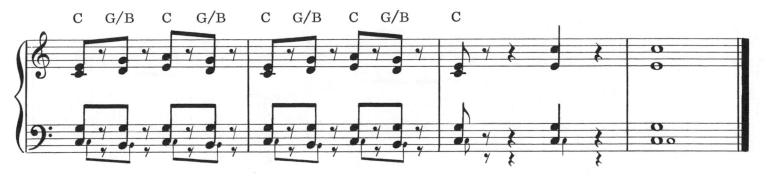

Faust Waltz Song

Charles Gounod

Charles Gounod's most famous opera, Faust, which had its premiere in Paris in 1859, is based on the drama by Johann Wolfgang von Goethe. Faust, an aging, embittered scholar, makes a pact with the devil, Mephistopheles (in the guise of a wealthy nobleman), to sell his soul in return for youth and pleasure. At first, his life is a charmed one. He falls in love with Marguerite, a beautiful and innocent young girl, tempting her with a gift of rich jewels (from Mephistopheles' hand, of course). Marguerite returns his love, whereupon Mephistopheles, furious at anyone else's happiness, steps in to bring sorrow and tragedy to all. One of the loveliest moments in Gounod's popular score is not an aria but a dance. The villagers are having a high-spirited time in the town square when this lovely waltz begins. The girls whirl by in their full-skirted dresses; the young men enthusiastically seize them by the waist and almost toss them into the air. A more romantic interlude is followed by the return of the buoyant leaping theme. While music of such joy and innocence is playing, the villagers remain unaware of the wicked charms of the ever-present, malevolent Mephistopheles.

Moderate, spirited waltz

16

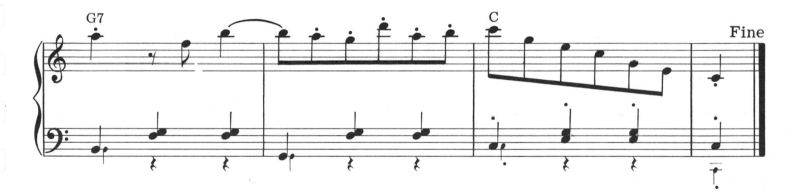

Là ci darem la mano

from **Don Giovanni**   Wolfgang Amadeus Mozart

Mozart called his 1787 opera Don Giovanni a comedy, despite the fact that its central character, the licentious Don Juan, dies in the flames of Hell. Don Juan has seduced so many beautiful women in the course of his career that his servant, Leporello, has to keep their names in a sizable notebook lest his master forget them all. (There are 1,003 names from Spain alone!) The Don, an unbridled sensualist looks upon every woman as a challenge, regardless of her background or experience. While trying to elude two women — Donna Anna, whose father he has murdered in a duel, and Donna Elvira, whose love he has betrayed — he spies a pretty peasant girl, Zerlina, and her country bumpkin of a lover. They are about to be married, but this doesn't deter the Don in any way. He persuades Leporello to get rid of the young man, while he himself effortlessly charms Zerlina with amorous glances, vague promises and sweet music. "Là ci darem la mano" ("Put your hand in mine"), he sings in their duet, "and I'll put mine in yours." In no time he has convinced the girl of his undying affection, and she, every thought of her rustic lover vanished, succumbs to her new suitor. First each sings to the other in this duet, and then they sing together (at the bottom of page 20, Don Juan's voice is heard in the left hand, Zerlina's in the right). The section ends with harmony and promise, and the final Allegro signifies triumph for him and surrender for her, the two voices harmonizing in graceful thirds.

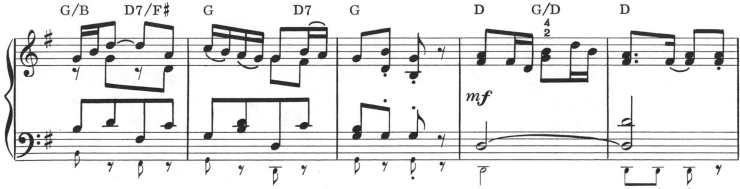

19

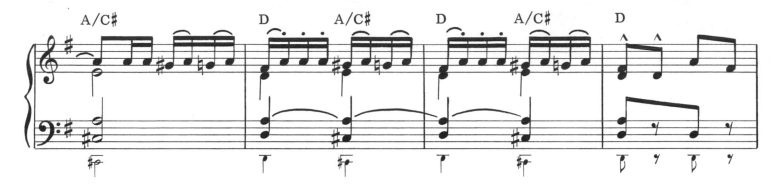

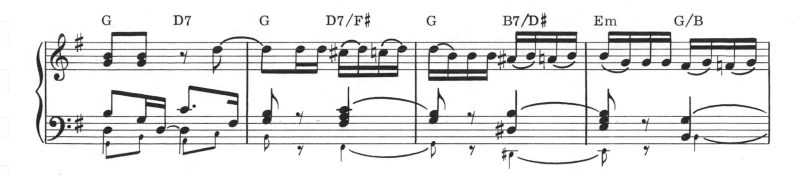

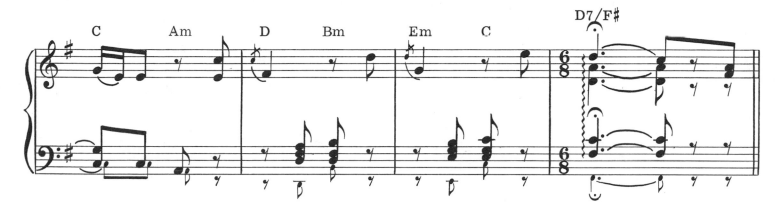

Allegro, in 2 (♩. = 1 beat)

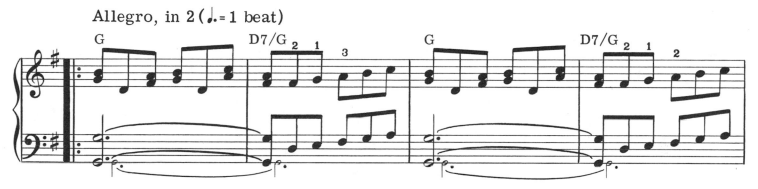

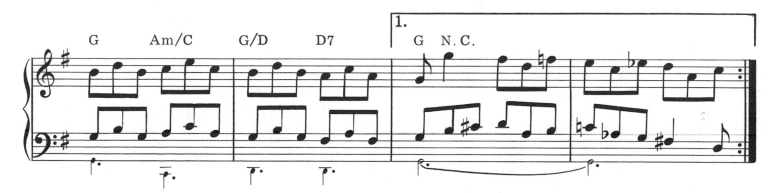

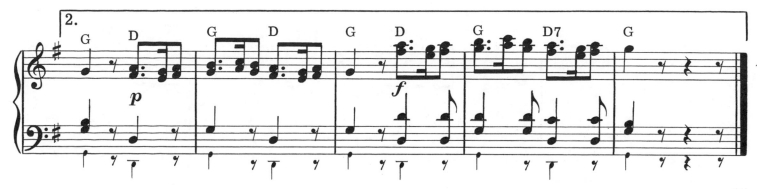

Vesti la giubba

Ruggiero Leoncavallo — *from* **I Pagliacci**

Leoncavallo's I Pagliacci, which was premiered to great success in Milan in 1892, is based on the "terrible truths" of love and jealousy in a traveling troupe of actors. Among the four members of the troupe are Canio, the leader, who plays

Pagliaccio the clown, and Nedda, his wife. Nedda is secretly in love with Silvio, who lives in the village they are presently visiting. Canio, jealous by nature and suspicious by habit, warns his wife about cheating on her marriage vows. The worst happens. Nedda and Silvio decide to elope, and Canio overhears their conversation. Beside himself with rage, Canio must nonetheless turn his mind to the evening's performance. As he dons his costume, he sings this famous aria, a particular favorite of the legendary tenor Enrico Caruso. "Vesti la giubba" ("On with the clown's motley"), he sings, despite the fact that underneath the comical outfit his heart is breaking. Dressed in the costumes of the traditional commedia dell'arte characters they represent, the actors find that their play has turned into reality. Before them and the horrified audience, Canio stabs his wife when she refuses to reveal the name of her lover . . . as Columbine, the character she is playing, also refuses in the drama they are enacting.

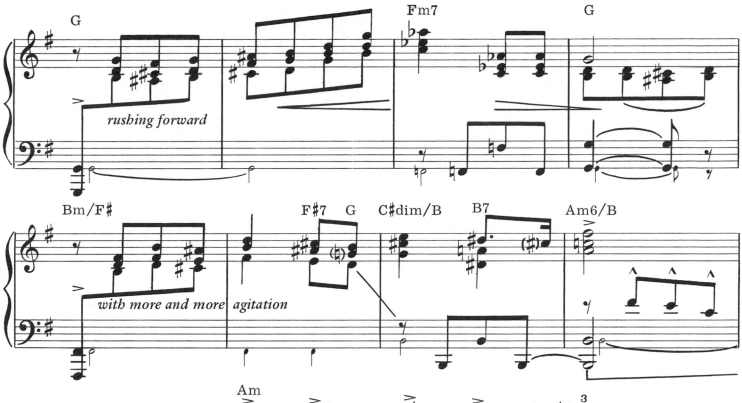

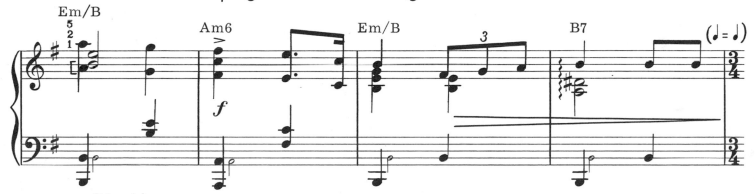

The Barber of Seville Overture

Gioacchino Rossini

Rossini composed his most famous opera, The Barber of Seville, in less than two weeks. With such a deadline, he fudged a little by incorporating into it music he had written earlier. Whether it was this fact or the ardent partisanship of the fans of Giovanni Paisiello, composer of another opera of the same name and plot, the opening-night audience was determined to ruin the premiere — and did so with whistling and shouts. The rabble's rude noises drowned out the entire second act, whereupon the 23-year-old Rossini, who was leading the performance from the piano, retired to his bed in a huff. But the second performance a day or so later was a blazing success. That audience left the theater and marched to the composer's house to fetch him and reward him with a huge party. Today the opera is still a hit with audiences around the world. The libretto is witty, and the score is enchantingly melodious, delicately characterized and subtly humorous. And, of course, there is the Overture (which Rossini had already used in two other operas), one of the world's most beloved, shining with tunes. The selection here is the piece's most melodic portion, displaying Rossini's superb sense of architecture, as the closing of even this shortened version of the original attests.

Allegro

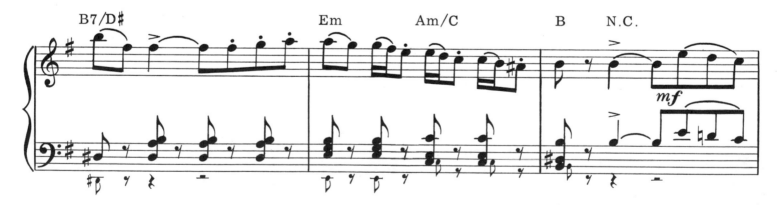

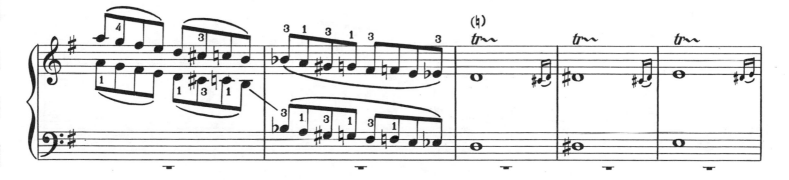

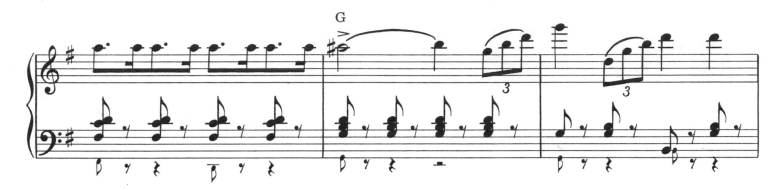

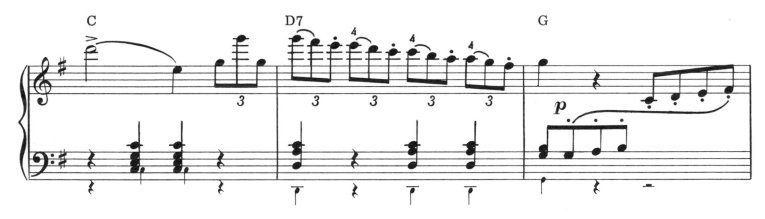

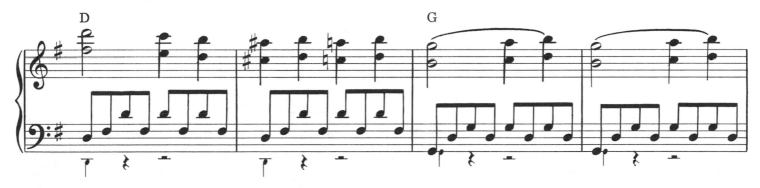

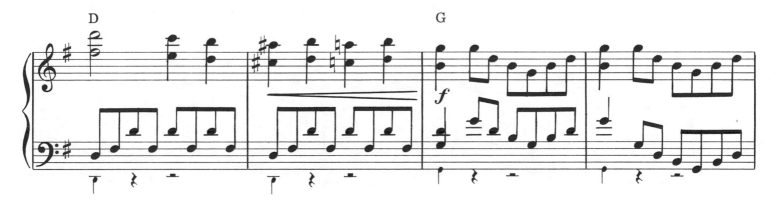

La Traviata: Prelude to Act 1

Giuseppe Verdi

In 1853, two very different Verdi operas, Il Trovatore and La Traviata, were performed for the first time. Il Trovatore, with its bloody, turgid plot laid in the 15th century, is melodramatic in the extreme. La Traviata (The Fallen Woman), on the other hand, gives us a believable, lovable, subtly drawn heroine in the courtesan Violetta, who coaxed from Verdi some of his most elegant, atmospheric music. (Violetta was also the inspiration for Alexander Dumas's La dame aux camellias, which in turn inspired the Greta Garbo film Camille.) The Prelude that Verdi composed for the first act not only sets the stage emotionally but almost tells the entire story. Its opening chords, mysterious, gray and poignant, suggest Violetta's

frail health, and its subsequent theme traces the hopelessness of her love for Alfredo, her weakness for a life of luxury, her noble sacrifice for the good of Alfredo's family. Franco Zeffirelli, in his stunning 1983 cinematic version of the opera, recognized the Prelude's storytelling possibilities and used it to accompany the flash-forward scenes of Violetta's unhappy end. As the music begins, the camera moves pensively through her almost empty apartment, where workmen are packing up her few remaining bits of furniture to appease her creditors. Throughout the film, as throughout the Prelude, the pathetic, once-beautiful face of Violetta stares at us, her ability to enchant dimmed but not extinguished.

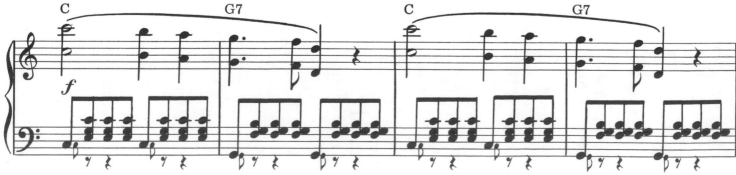

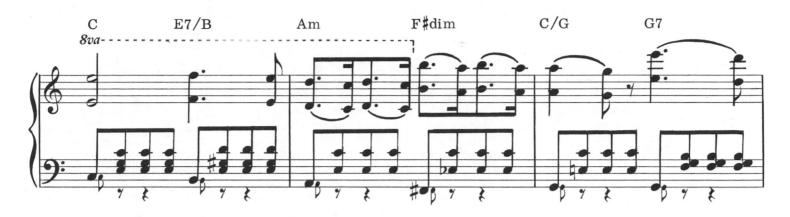

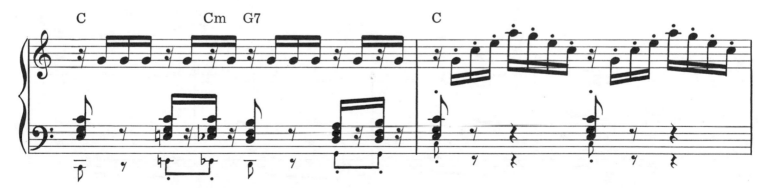

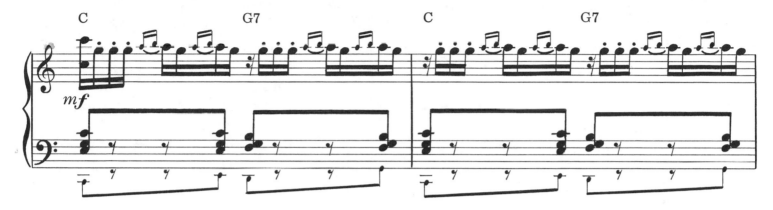

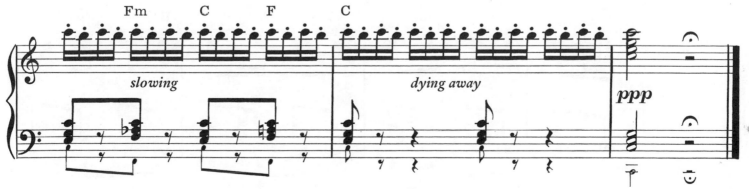

The Bartered Bride Polka

Bedřich Smetana

Smetana's The Bartered Bride is a distinctively Czech opera and a jauntily refreshing one, too. Smetana's music is based on folk themes, and the libretto is equally authentic, so it is surprising that the work did not win admirers at its premiere in Prague in 1866. Nevertheless, Smetana's countrymen did not accept the opera until its third performance, and only when The Bartered Bride was presented in Vienna, in 1892, did it become the hugely popular repertoire staple that it is today. It is an opera full of dances. This Polka, added by the composer for the opera's Paris debut in 1869, comes early in the story, when the villagers are celebrating a church festival. Before long, the

plot will involve Mařenka (who is in love with Jeník and he with her), her parents and a greedy marriage broker. The parents and the broker insist that Mařenka must marry the goodhearted but simpleminded son of a rich landowner rather than Jeník. In the end, of course, everything comes out right, since Jeník turns out to be the long-lost oldest son of the same rich man. Meanwhile, we have been treated to many more folk dances. Most are like this polka — bristling with tightly reined energy or contrasted with a leisurely swinging motif.

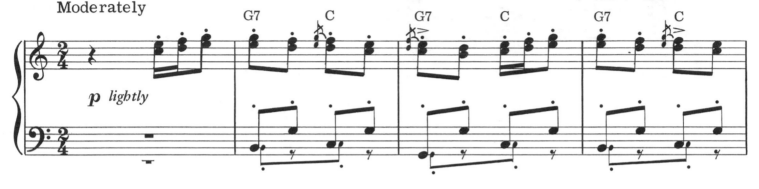

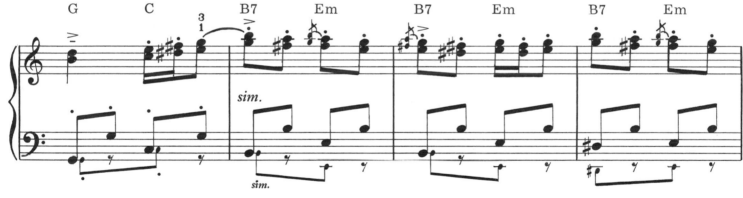

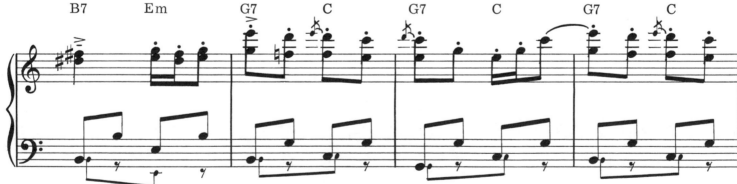

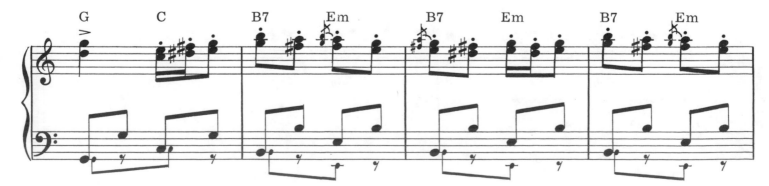

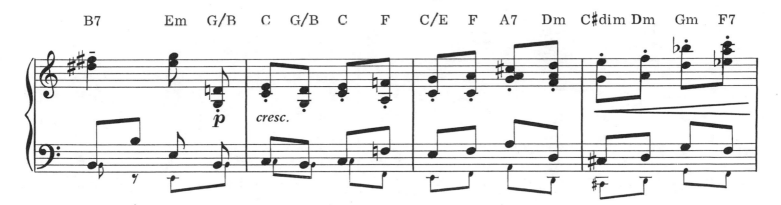

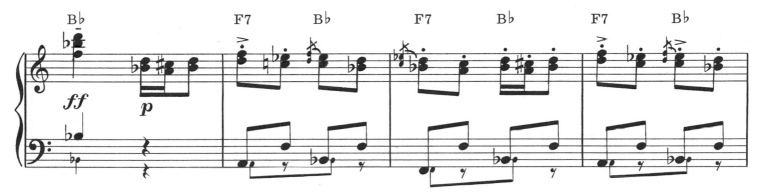

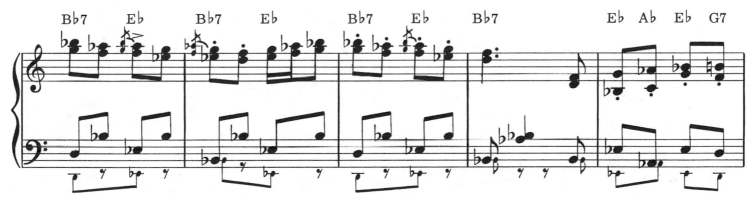

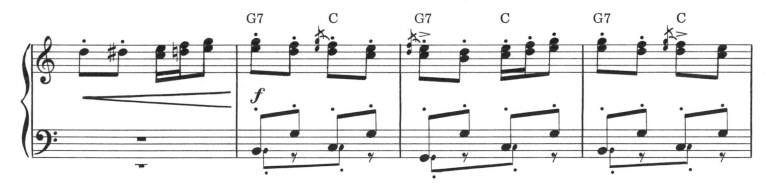

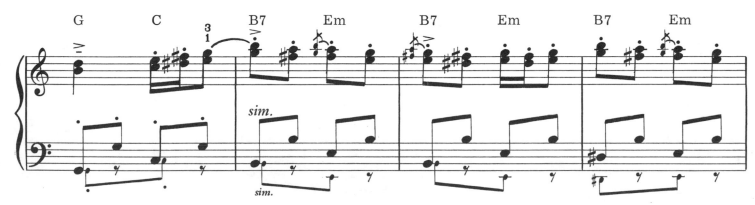

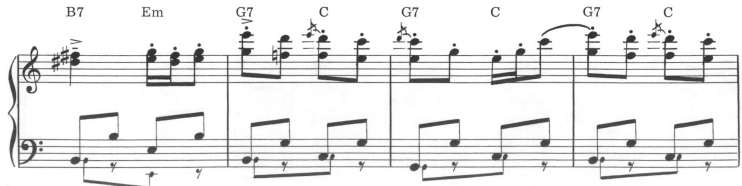

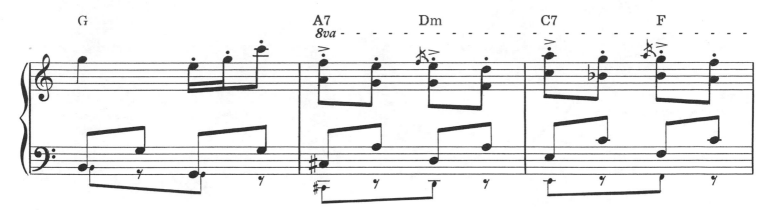

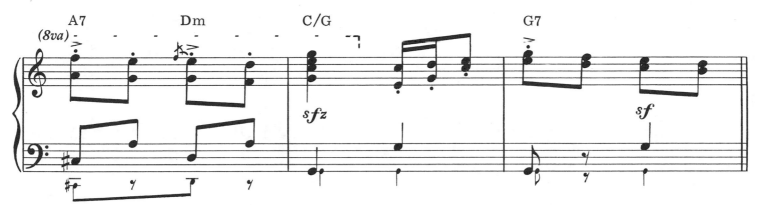

Flower Song

from **Carmen**
Georges Bizet

Slowly, but not dragging

* No organ pedal till bar 21.

Many at the premiere of Bizet's **Carmen** in Paris in 1875 were repulsed by the savage passions of the story and the enormously sensual music. Only in later performances did the work begin to achieve the reputation it has today as one of the most popular operas ever written. In it, Carmen, a Spanish Gypsy girl who works in a cigarette factory, seduces men and then quickly tires of them. When Don José, an army corporal, first sees her, she is singing the well-known "Habanera" with passionate intensity. To taunt the seemingly indifferent José, Carmen flings a rose in his face.

When she is arrested for brawling, he helps her escape and falls irrevocably in love with her. He runs away with her, destroying his army career. Later, when Carmen has rejected him for another man and is mocking him, he pulls out the remnants of the rose she tossed when they met and sings this "Flower Song." The aria is delicate in outline yet grows to a superb climax, after which the music reverts to the first melody and the muted ending chords that presage José's final frenzy of jealous passion, during which he stabs to death the girl who has so nonchalantly ruined his life.

Flower Song from **Carmen**

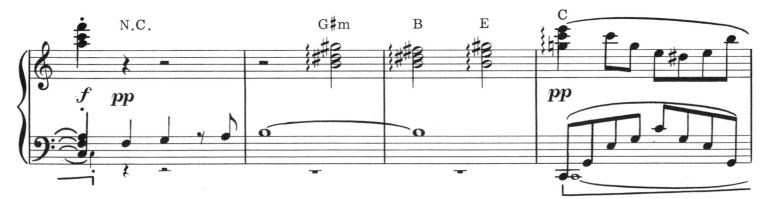

Dance of the Hours

Ponchielli's La Gioconda (1876) tells a murky tale of betrayal and treachery during the 17th-century Inquisition in Venice. The tale at one point is interrupted — and redeemed, many think — by a charming ballet, the "Dance of the Hours." Somehow the opera's heroine, an impecunious street singer, finds herself in the ballroom of a glittering palazzo, where richly masked and costumed guests take turns dancing with the ballet troupe. In Ponchielli's day, dance was considered a necessary part of grand opera, and the classical theme based on the passage of the times of the day appealed to both the composer and his audience. In the ballet, the dewy freshness of morning is followed by the energy of noon, the richness of afternoon and finally the gaiety of evening. The selection here offers the restrained charm of daylight's elegant phrases. Long a favorite in the concert hall, "Dance of the Hours" found a new, hilarious interpretation in Walt Disney's animated film classic Fantasia (1940), in which it is "danced" by ungainly ostriches, crocodiles and hippopotamuses.

from **La Gioconda**   Amilcare Ponchielli

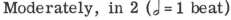

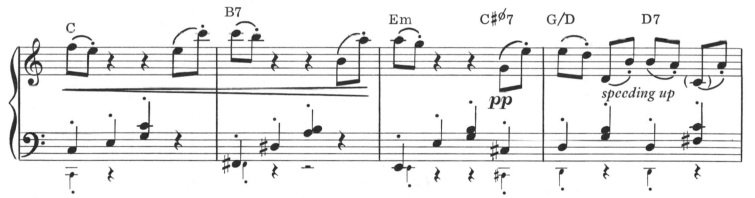

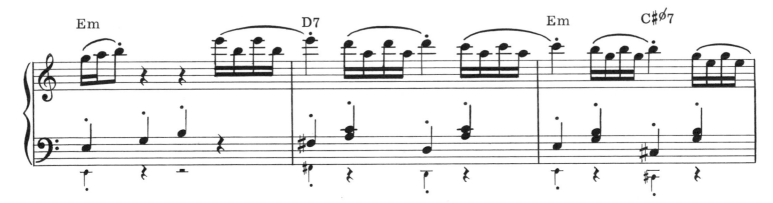

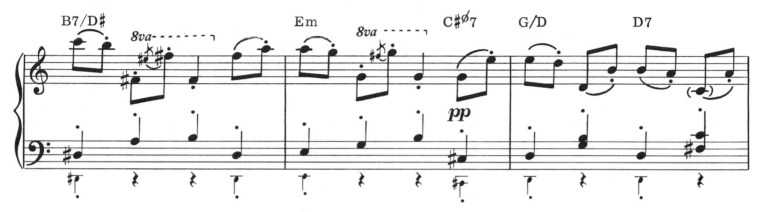

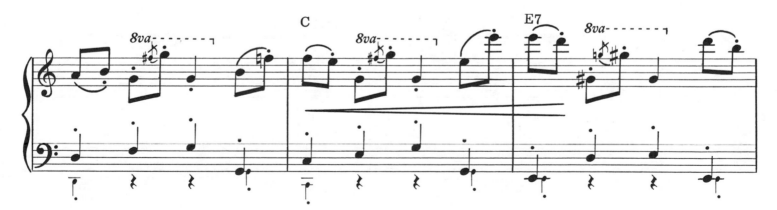

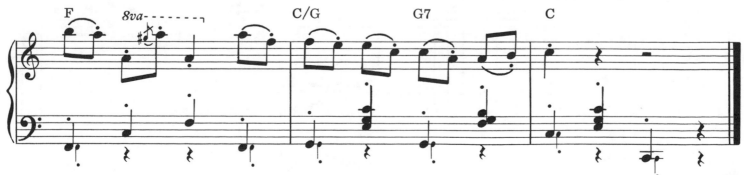

2
Popular Classics
from
Storybook Places

Scheherazade Highlights

(The Young Prince and Princess)

Nicolai Rimsky-Korsakov
Arranged by Dan Fox

In composing his symphonic suite Scheherazade, Nicolai Rimsky-Korsakov drew for musical inspiration on his own genius and the music of Russian Asia. Inspiration for the setting came from the collection of Persian stories we know as The Thousand and One Nights. His masterpiece equals those evocative tales in imagination and sweep. The stories center on a handsome young king who has had his wife executed because of her wantonness and treachery. Determined to avenge himself on all women, he marries a different one each night. But, the next morning, no matter how much he has enjoyed her company, he orders her beheaded. Finally, the beautiful, intelligent and cunning Scheherazade offers herself as a candidate. The first night she seeks to please her royal husband by telling him a story. One tale leads to another and then another, until he falls into a romantic sleep. The next morning he obviously cannot behead Scheherazade because he must hear the end of the tale. His new wife accedes to his demand for more stories but carefully avoids finishing the last one . . . and so it goes for a thousand and one nights, until the young man realizes her ruse. By that time it is too late; he has become convinced of Scheherazade's worthiness and has grown to love her. In the suite that bears her name, Scheherazade can be recognized in the plaintive line played in the orchestra by a solo violin (here, it is the opening line of the "Scheherazade theme" below). Her motif always leads to a new story. The section arranged here tells of the love of a prince for a princess. The princess (her theme begins on page 41; the prince's on page 44) is innocent and charming as she moves gracefully to the jingling of tambourines. Then the music moves to G major, and one of the world's great romantic themes begins — simple and heartfelt yet with exotic little passages of running sixteenth notes that remind us of the Near Eastern inspiration from which Rimsky-Korsakov worked.

Scheherazade theme

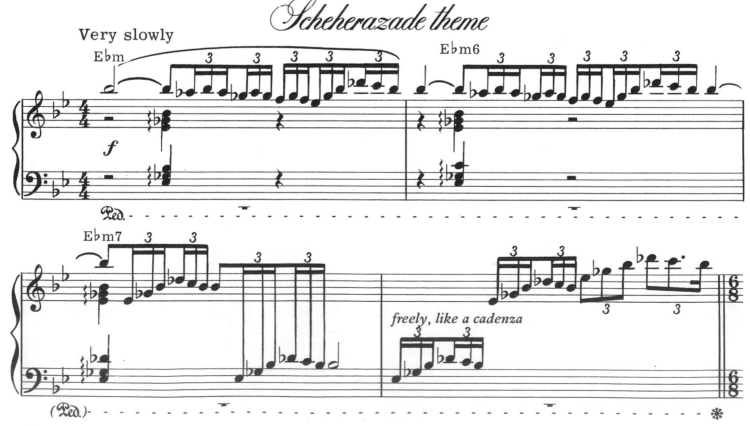

The Princess

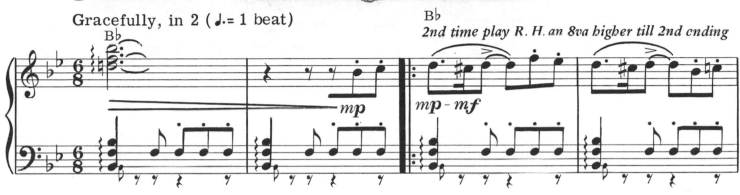

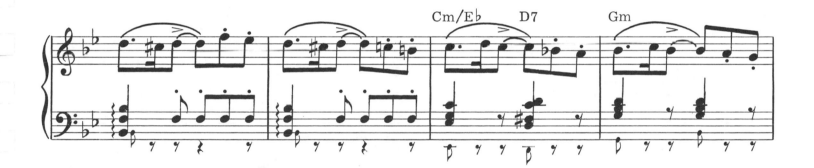

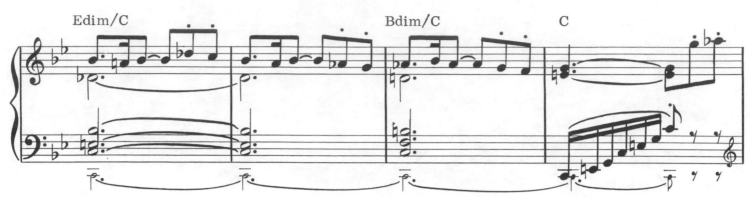

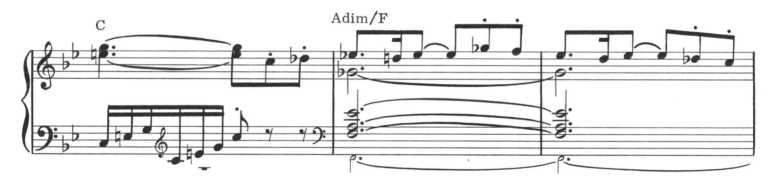

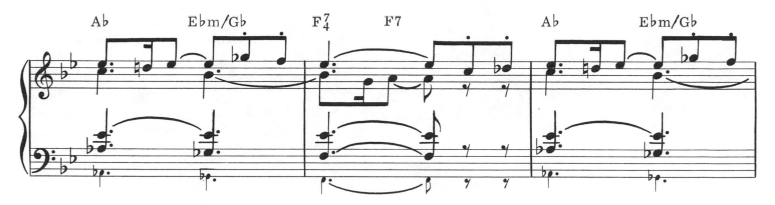

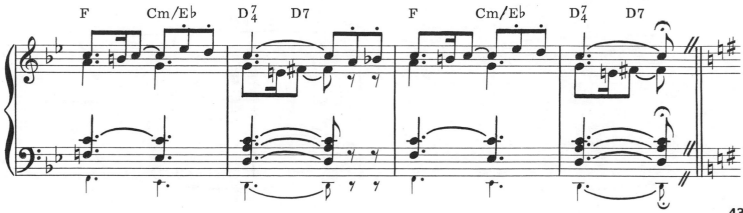

The Prince

Flowing, still in 2

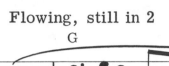

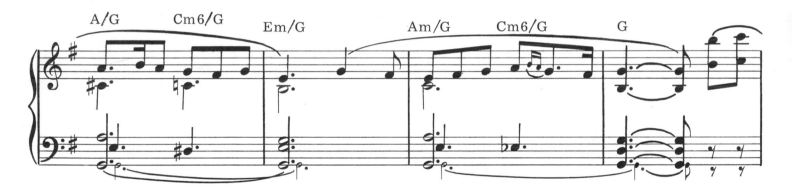

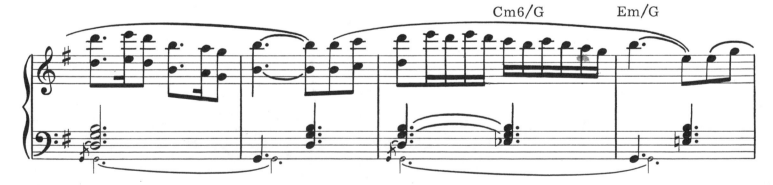

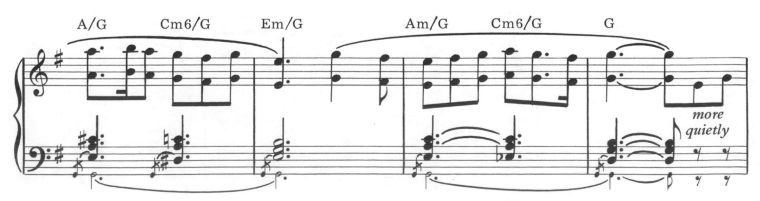

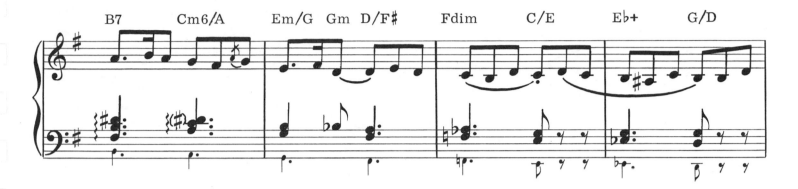

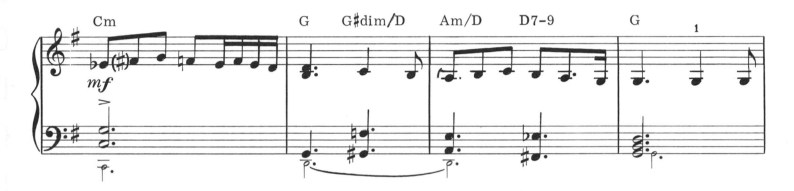

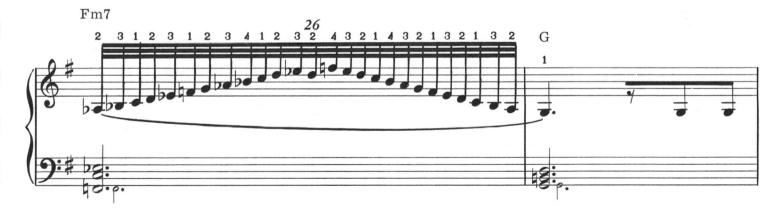

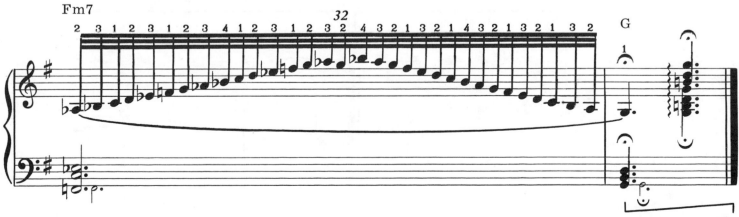

The Boccherini Minuet

Luigi Boccherini

Born in Lucca, Italy, in 1743, Boccherini grew up in a musical family. He not only learned to play the cello at an early age, he also began to write music — music of all sorts — from pieces for the town band to oratorios for the local church. He traveled for much of his life and, until his last years, found a warm welcome and financial rewards wherever he went. He completed approximately 500 works, among them more than 100 quintets for string instruments. One of these, published in 1775, for two violins, viola and two cellos, included this graceful, elegant Minuet. Movie enthusiasts will recognize it as the piece practiced over and over by Alec Guinness and his bumbling partners in crime in the film **The Ladykillers**. Part of the Minuet's piquancy derives from its first two phrases, in which the melody is played in syncopated fashion, on the offbeat.

Moderately

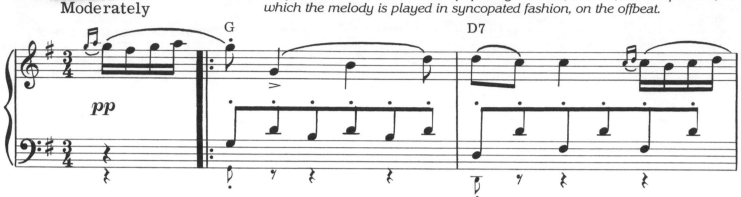

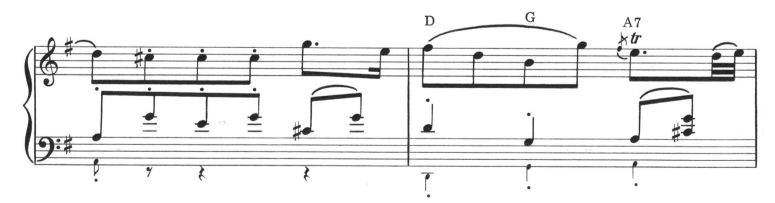

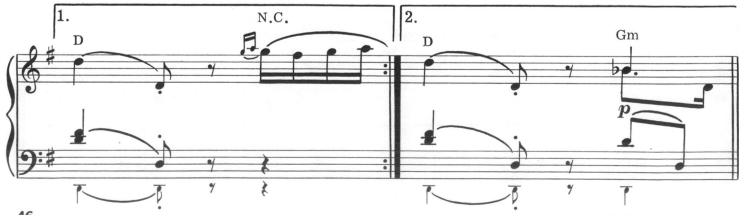

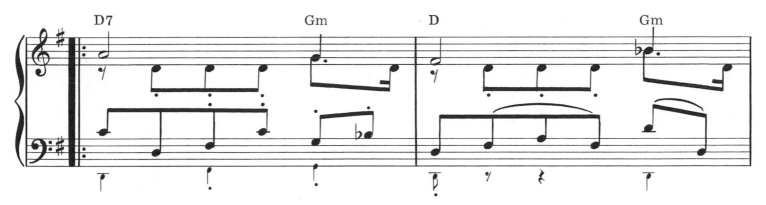

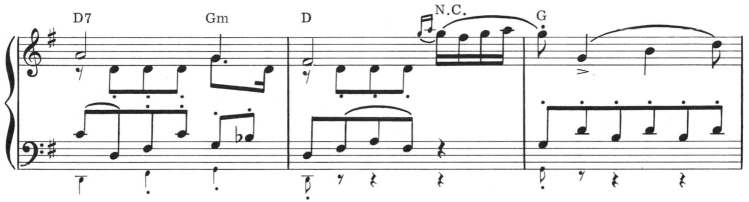

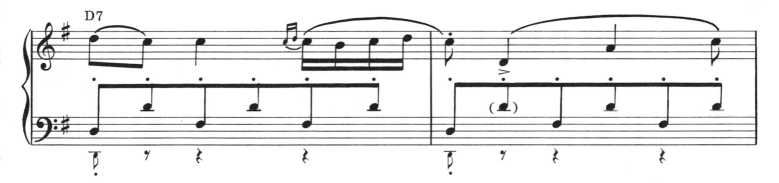

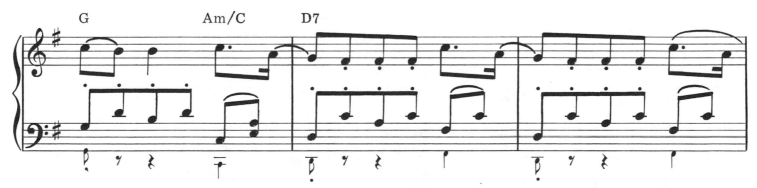

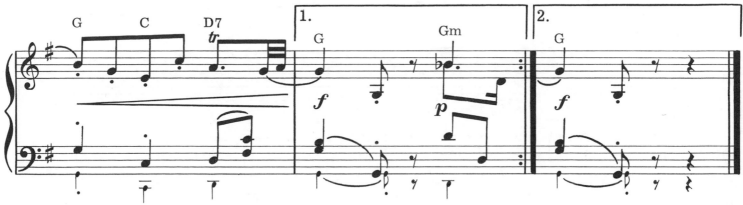

Hungarian Dance No. 1

Johannes Brahms

The great German composer Johannes Brahms spent his youth in the port city of Hamburg, where he played the piano in low taverns and bars to eke out his family's meager income. Such was his genius, however, that he was soon known among the great musicians of the city. One of these was the Hungarian violinist Eduard Reményi, who engaged the 20-year-old to accompany him on a concert tour of Hungary. This was the first time that Brahms had been exposed to Gypsy and Magyar music; it was to influence him for the rest of his life. Sixteen years later, in 1869, he published his first set of **Hungarian Dances**. These piano duets were arrangements of Hungarian folk tunes and dances he had heard while traveling with Reményi. "Dance No. 1," arranged here, begins with a romantic surging theme, as if some Gypsy horseman were plunging through the hills with the wind whistling around him. In the second part, the pace becomes even faster, and the racing sixteenth notes of the last line push forward, each set of four accented, to make a brilliant conclusion.

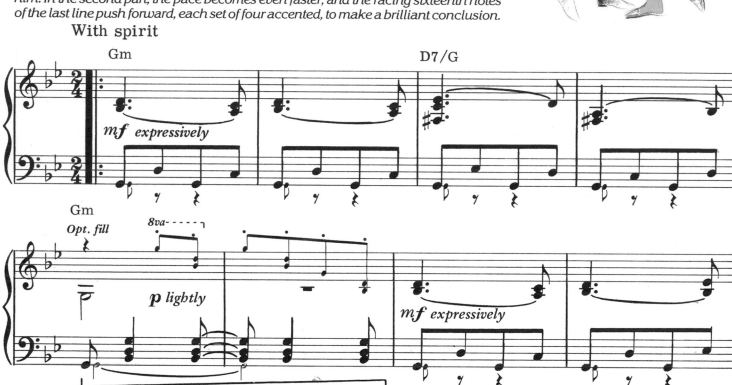

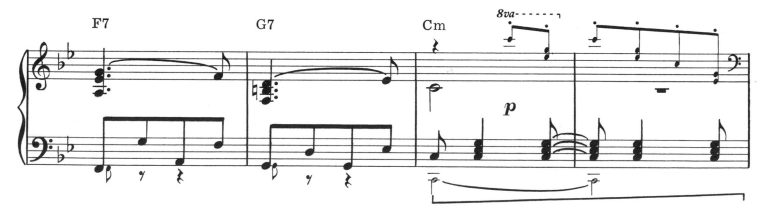

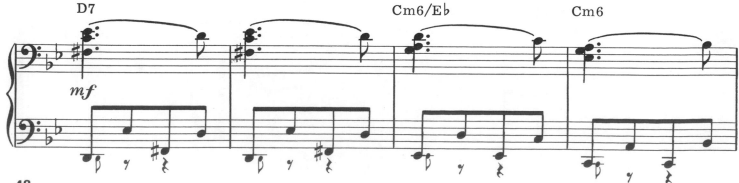

48

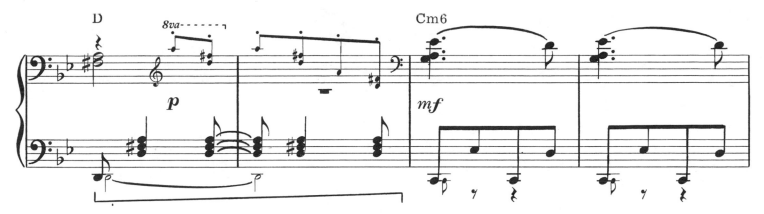

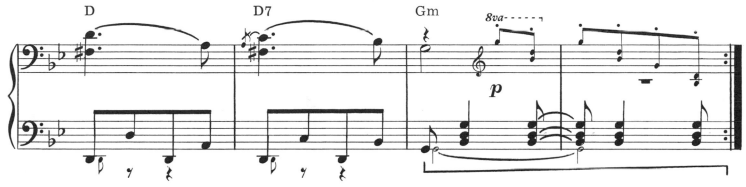

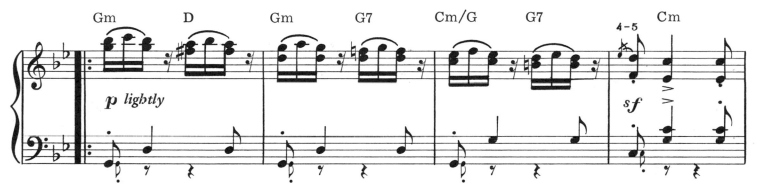

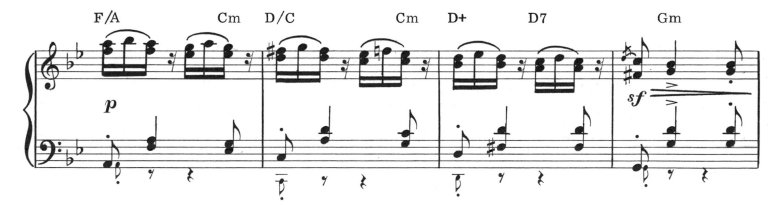

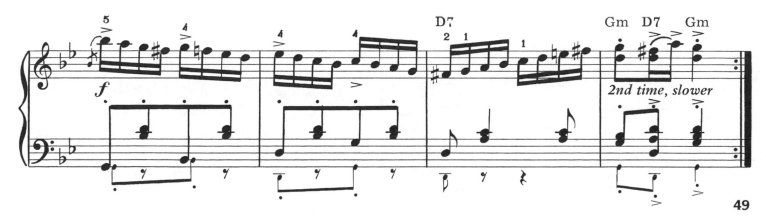

Andaluza
(Spanish Dance No. 5)

Enrique Granados

Enrique Granados was one of the first Spanish composers of the Romantic era to derive nearly all of his musical inspiration from his homeland, with its varying provinces, each with its own history, legends, dance and music. Granados' Danzas Españolas (Spanish Dances), of which "Andaluza" is the fifth, made him famous when they were published in the late 1890s. He was then a young man, in his 20s, and succeeding works only increased his fame. The beautiful melodies that brought Granados public acclaim also aroused the admiration of Pablo Casals. So enthusiastic was the great

Spanish cellist that he dubbed his countryman "the Spanish Schubert." "Andaluza" recalls Andalusia, a region of southern Spain bordering on the Mediterranean. The piece, also called "Playera," is Granados' refined version of the ancient Spanish dance and song of that name. After a guitar prelude (to mimic the sound of a guitar, play the sequence with very little pedal, if any), a song of love begins, in short phrases at first and then a long one. This is the form of the playera. The composer added a lovely romantic section, changing the E-minor key to major, before allowing the guitar theme to reassert itself. Tragically, Granados and his wife were drowned in 1916 when they were returning to Spain from New York. They had come to witness the American premiere of his opera Goyescas, also based on Spanish dances, at the Metropolitan Opera House. Delaying their voyage back so that Granados could perform for President Woodrow Wilson at the White House, they changed passage to a ship that would take them home via England. En route, the ship was torpedoed by a German submarine.

Andantino quasi allegretto
(Moving along, but not too fast)

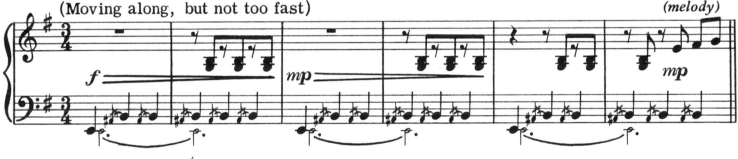

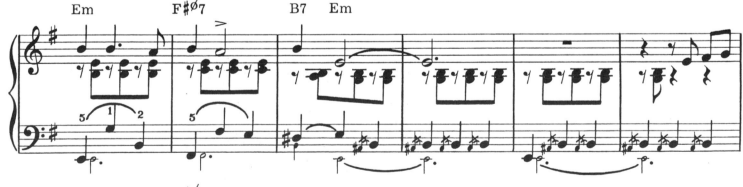

50

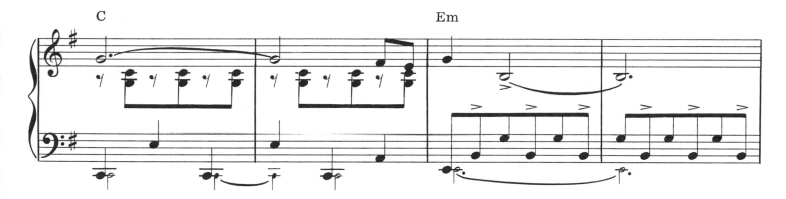

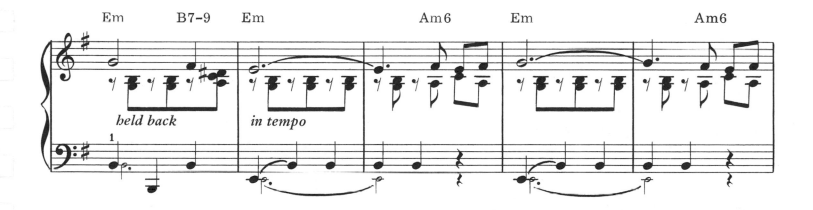

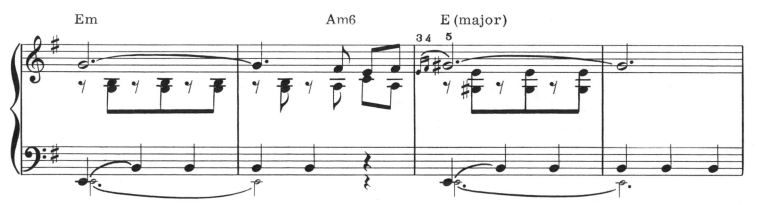

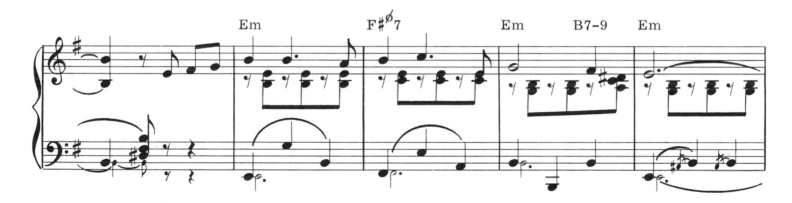

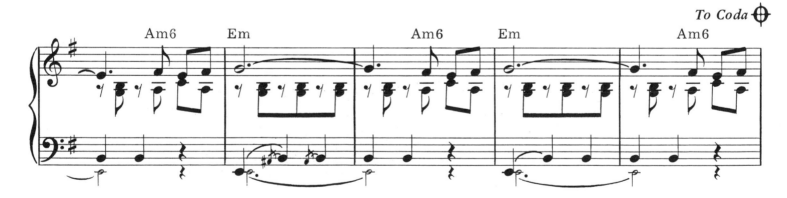

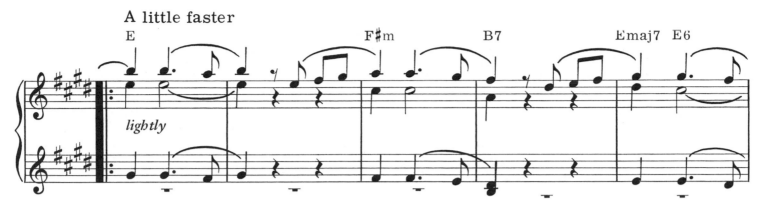

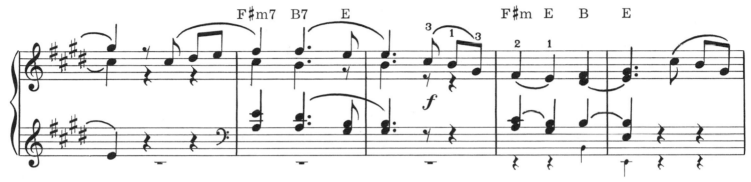

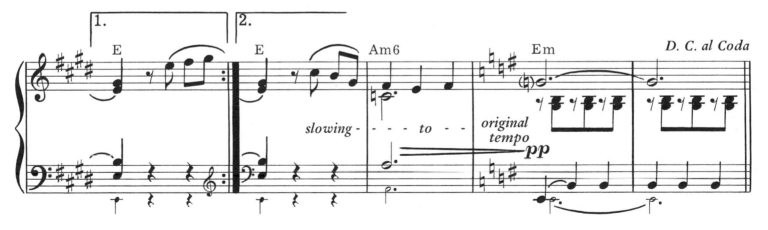

Slavonic Dance No. 1

Antonín Dvořák

Antonín Dvořák became the first Bohemian composer to make the folk tunes of his native land familiar to the world. This "Dance No. 1" from his Slavonic Dances, for example, is a Bohemian dance with an interesting rhythmic character-istic. After the opening chord—a one-note fanfare—the melody falls into two-measure groupings, at first the six beats divide into three long accented ones and then into six shorter ones, after which the pattern is repeated. The middle section seems to change but actually retains the rhythm, only becoming more lyrical. Then the first theme returns, more energetic than ever, until a running pattern of eighth notes makes an increasingly thinner texture leading to the final measures, whose fortissimo echoes the opening note.

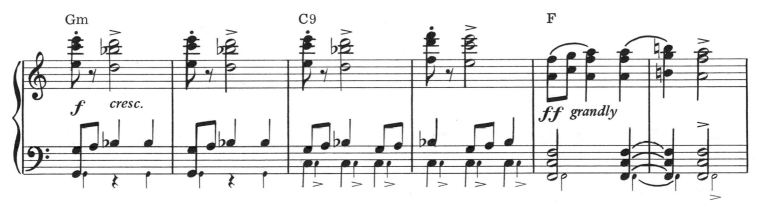

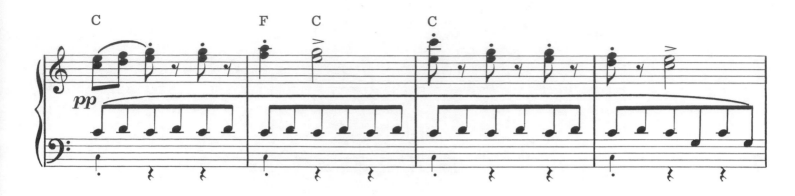

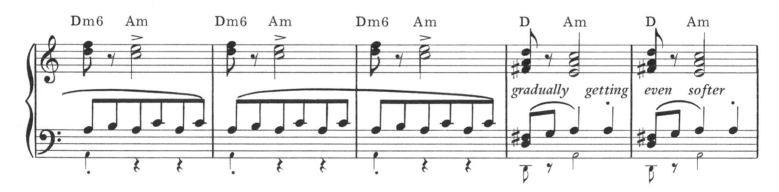

Pavane for a Dead Princess

Maurice Ravel

One of Maurice Ravel's early successes was his "Pavane for a Dead Princess" ("Pavane pour une infante défunte"), which was published in 1899, supposedly in honor of a Spanish princess who had died young. (Ravel's mother may have been a Basque whose family came from the French region just to the north of the Iberian Peninsula, and although he himself never visited Spain for any significant period of time, he wrote several of his finest compositions under the influence of its culture.) The pavane is an old dance, probably dating from the 16th century in Italy, and may derive its name from the Italian word for "peacock" or from the town of Padua. In dancing it, the feet were kept low to the ground, and the tempo was stately and ceremonial. Long famous as a work for pianists, the "Pavane" also furnished the melody for a popular song of the 1930s, when Tin Pan Alley songwriters were raiding classical music for tunes. The song was "The Lamp Is Low," with sultry lyrics by Mitchell Parish.

Maurice Ravel

Slowly

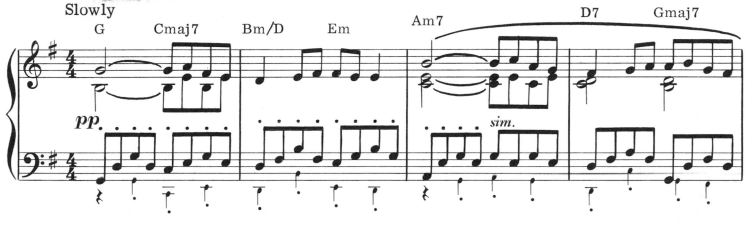

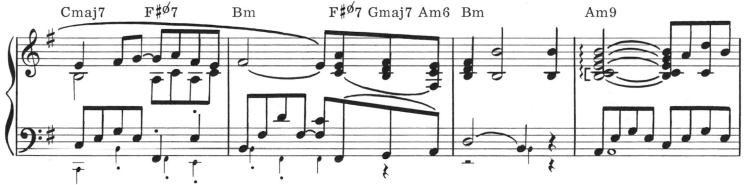

* That is, an E chord with the 3rd omitted.

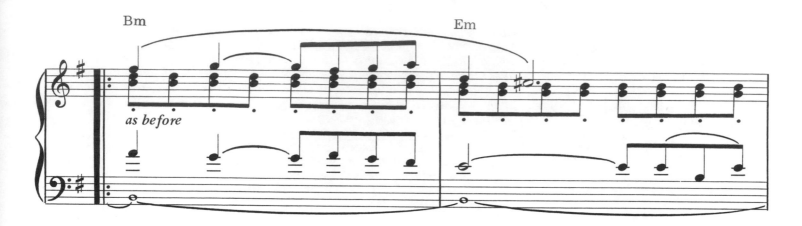

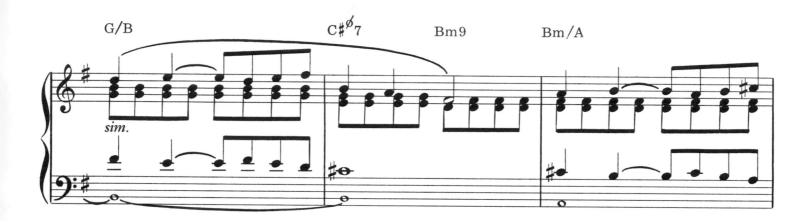

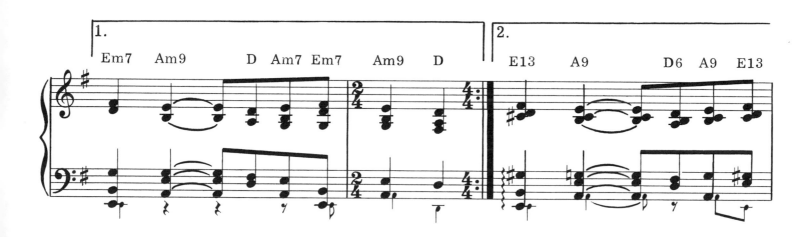

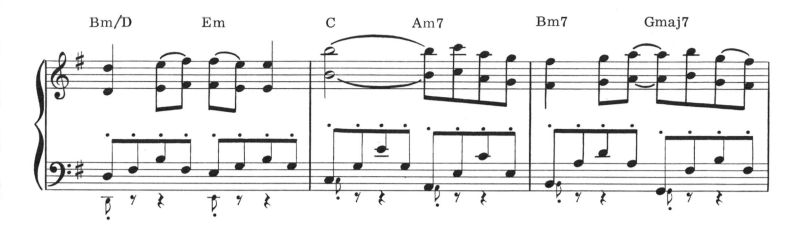

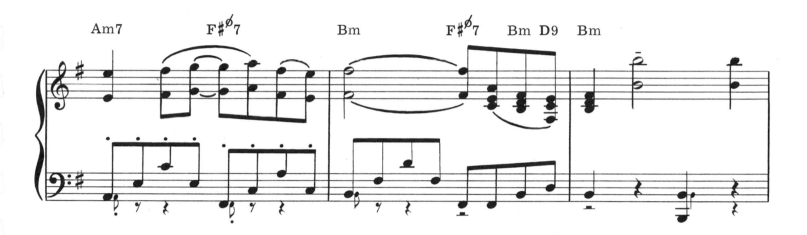

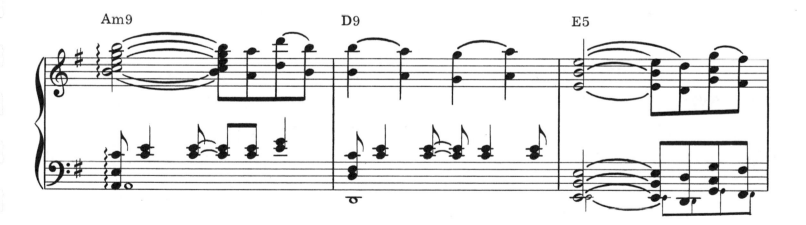

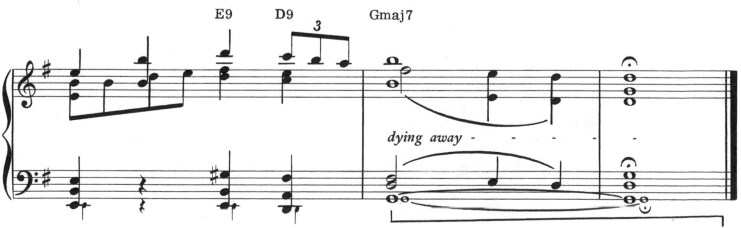

Peer Gynt Mini-Suite

Edvard Grieg

Edvard Grieg's **Peer Gynt** tells the story of an intelligent but selfish man who leaves his home and sweetheart to roam the world in search of adventure. This mini-suite starts with the charming pastorale "Morning," with the sounds (play them with the right hand on page 61) of a young shepherd piping to his sheep as dawn comes to the green Norwegian hills and an echo or two from the valleys below. In "Anitra's Dance," set in the African desert, Anitra seduces Peer with her dancing, her gossamer scarves caressing his face, her quick movements alternating with ecstatic themes of yearning double thirds. (You can hear the clicking of her castenets in the right-hand trills.) In the last excerpt, "In the Hall of the Mountain King," the traveler comes upon the powerful king of the trolls and his hundreds of subjects, who live in a network of tunnels lit by guttering lamps. When the trolls see Peer, they begin a menacing dance, quiet at first, then slowly mounting in excitement and fury until the music explodes in repeated cymbal crashes.

Morning

Anitra's Dance

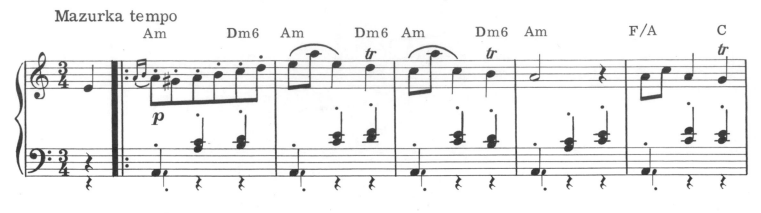

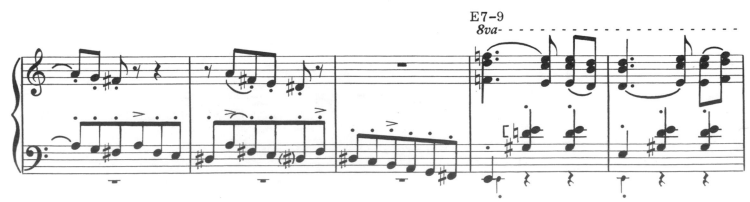

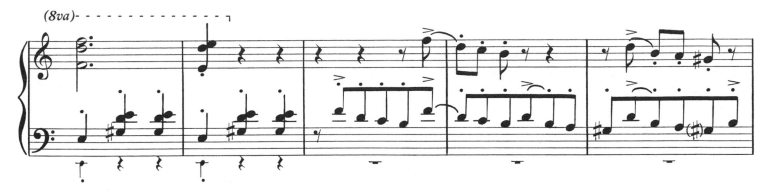

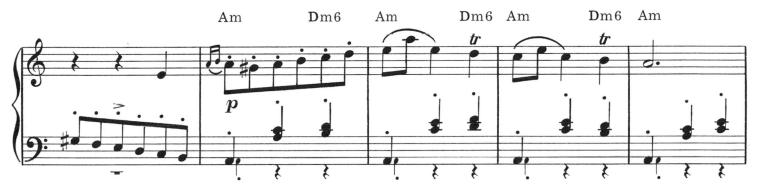

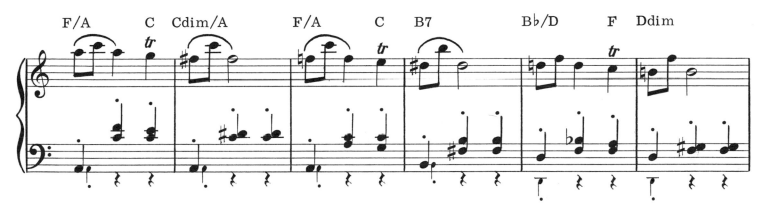

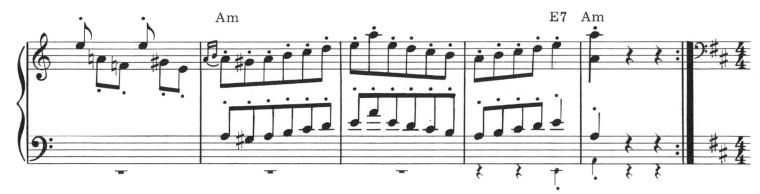

In the Hall of the Mountain King

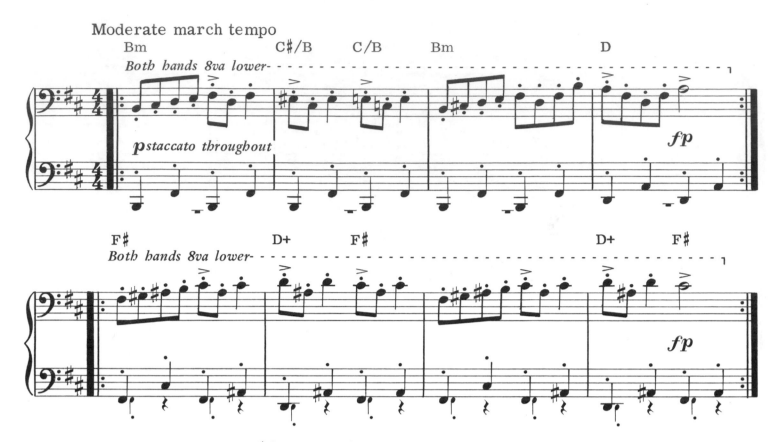

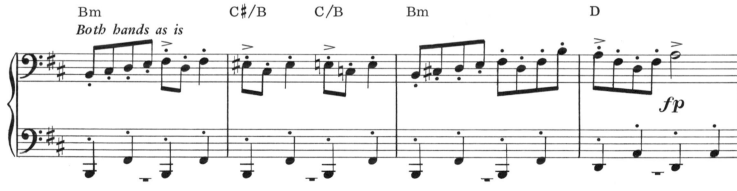

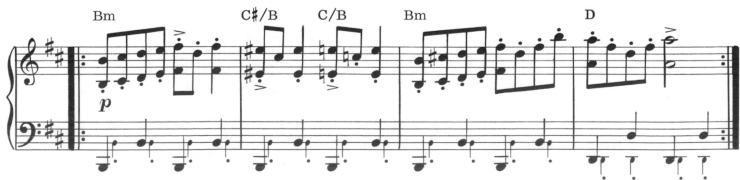

The birth of stereo in the 1950s unleashed a storm of often bizarre creativity among record producers. All at once, everyone had an idea for the stereo recording to end all stereo recordings, showing off the tonal range and wall-to-wall spread a listener's ears could now perceive. Overnight, the market bulged with records featuring the sounds of trains, boats and planes, automobile races, 101 strings and, most of all, brass instruments — massed drum-and-bugle corps, 76 trombones, even the combined brass sections of three top symphony orchestras playing the antiphonal music of the 16th-century Venetian master

Giovanni Gabrieli. Leroy Anderson's recording of his own piece, "Bugler's Holiday," featuring a trio of trumpeters, came close to being a chart-topper. One record company's brass showcase album from those days featured music by the French-born composer Leo Arnaud. It came to the attention of the American Broadcasting Company just as the network was completing its plans to televise the 1964 Olympics. As a result, this fanfare piece (also known as "Bugler's Dream") from the album, which punctuated ABC's coverage of that year's games and all games thereafter, is now widely accepted as the not-quite-official theme of the Olympics.

3
New and Old Classics from Film, Radio and TV

Olympic Fanfare

Leo Arnaud
TV Theme of the Olympic Games

Moderate march tempo

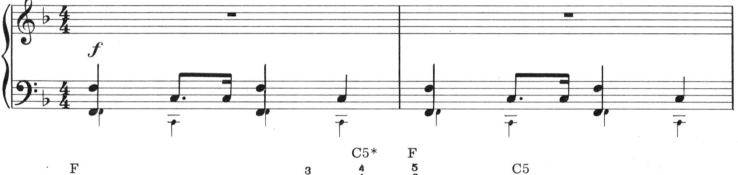

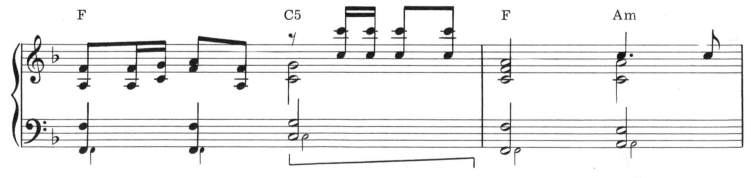

* C5 = a C chord with the 3rd omitted; the open 5th, C–G.

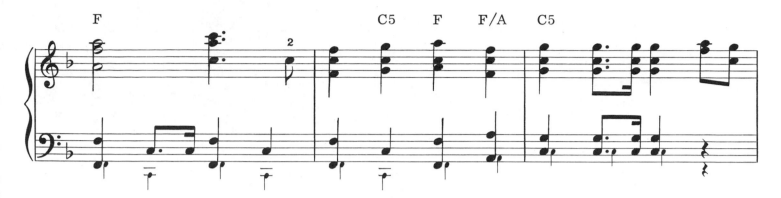

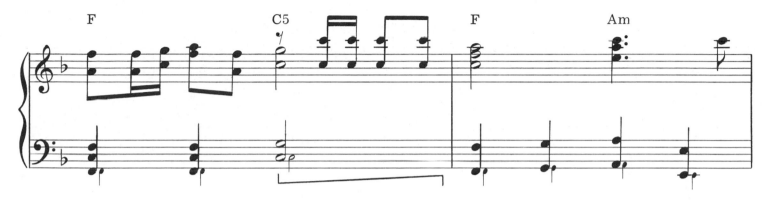

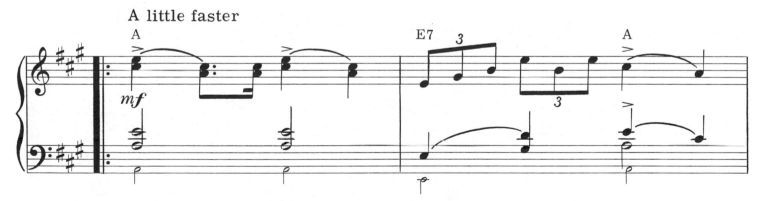

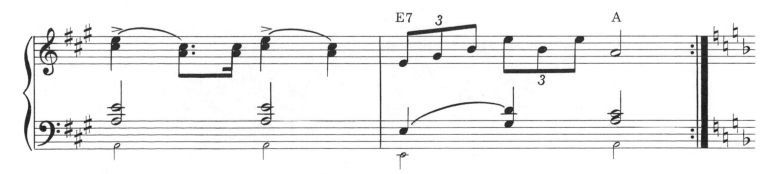

1st tempo

Harlem Nocturne

Earle Hagen

Mike Hammer *TV Theme*

What sound better evokes a big city at night — especially New York — than this lonely, smoky-torchy melody? Though "Harlem Nocturne" is perhaps most often heard played either by alto sax or trumpet, its composer was a trombonist named Earle Hagen, who did his Swing Era apprenticeship with such top bandleaders as Tommy Dorsey and Ray Noble. By 1940 he had settled in Hollywood and was writing music for movies while doubling as a sideman with Noble, playing for radio shows featuring such stars as George Burns and Gracie Allen. He wrote "Harlem

Nocturne" for Noble's saxophonist Jack Dumont, but trumpet playing bandleaders Harry James and Randy Brooks liked its soaring, rangy melodic line and picked it up. Brooks, in fact, used it as a theme during his brief, brilliant bandleading career cut tragically short by a stroke. During the '50s and '60s, Hagen's inner-city tone poem was heard often on movie and TV sound tracks, usually played by a wailing alto sax. But it seemed to fade after that — until its use in the mid-1980s as the theme for the TV detective series Mike Hammer gave it renewed exposure and popularity.

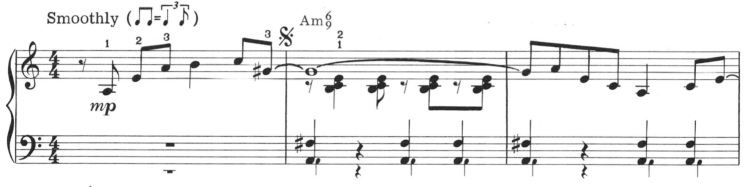

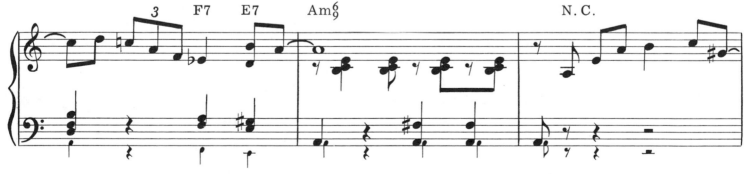

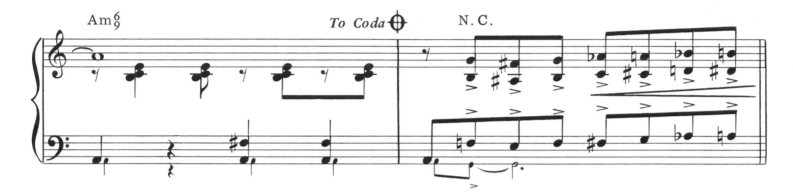

Am (add 9)

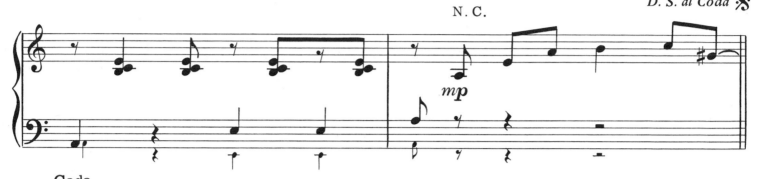

N. C.

D. S. al Coda 𝄋

Coda

D9 (add 6)

Am   N. C.

lightly

Symphony No. 4 ("Italian")

Felix Mendelssohn

Used in Breaking Away

Felix Mendelssohn was only 21 when he began composing his fourth symphony in 1830, but he was already a significant figure in the music world of his time. Among the works he composed while still a teenager are at least two masterpieces: the Octet for Strings, done at age 16, and the Overture to *A Midsummer Night's Dream,* written the following year. The idea for the "Italian" symphony came to him, appropriately enough, on a beach in Italy. The opening movement (here, for easier playing, transposed from A to G), used so effectively in the bicycle-race scenes in the 1979 film *Breaking Away,* works like an overture: It introduces all the merriment, color and energy that suffuses the entire work.

Quickly, with spirit (♩. = 1 beat)

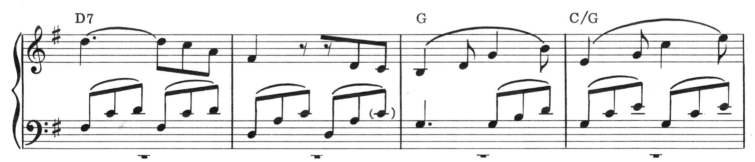

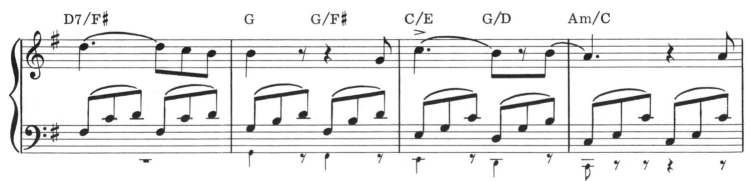

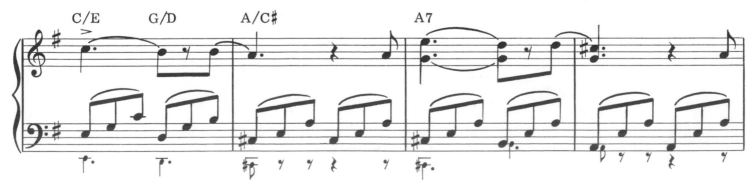

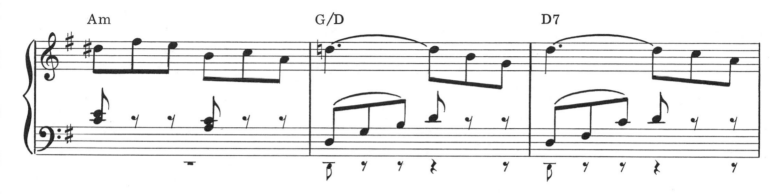

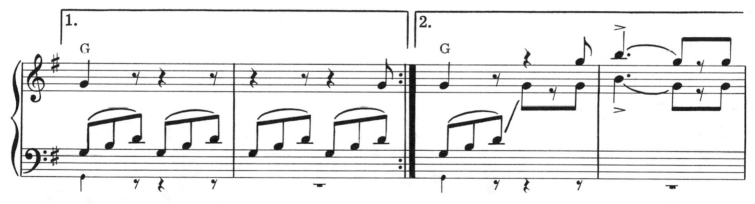

The Liberty Bell

John Philip Sousa

Monty Python TV Theme

It's interesting to speculate how America's revered "March King," John Philip Sousa, would have responded had he known that someday just a few notes of this stirring march would evoke smiles and even outright laughter. From all reports, Sousa was a rather austere man, correct and given to formality. Perhaps that makes the use of "The Liberty Bell" by John Cleese, Terry Gilliam and the rest of the madcap crew from the British TV show Monty Python all the funnier. Like so many of Sousa's best marches ("The High School Cadets" and "National Fencibles" for cadet competitions; "The Washington Post" for the newspaper), "The Liberty Bell" commemorates something specific, in this case a parade in honor of the return of the touring Liberty Bell to Philadelphia. Sousa wrote it in 1893 for the concert band that he formed after he resigned as conductor of the U.S. Marine Band. "The Liberty Bell" has long been a favorite of school bands, perhaps because it's easier to play than such later and somewhat better-known Sousa marches as "El Capitan" and "The Stars and Stripes Forever."

March tempo, in 2 (♩.=1 beat)

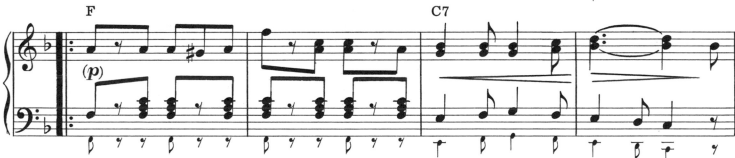

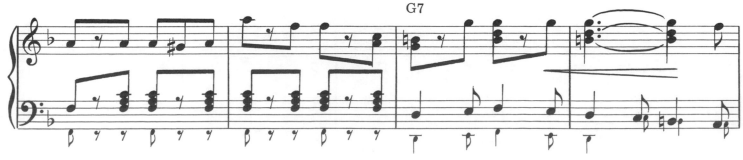

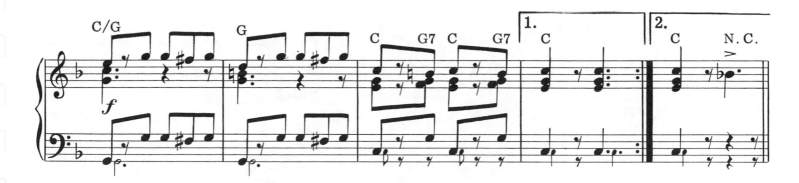

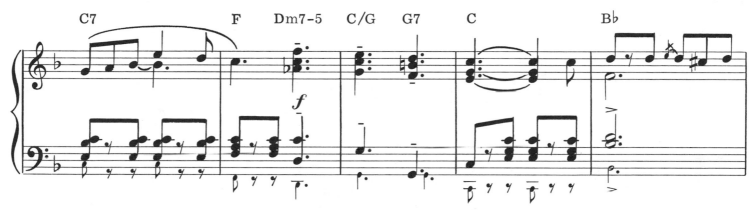

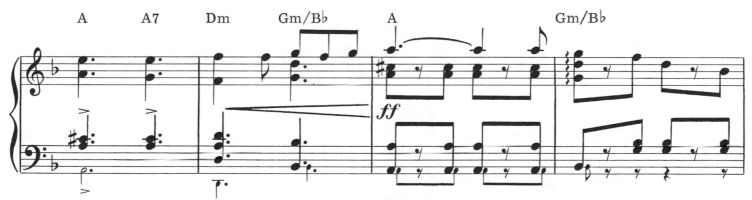

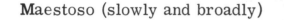

Here's a melody that most people know but few realize they know. Anyone who has seen a cowboys-and-Indians movie has heard it as background music when the Apaches or Sioux or Comanches are preparing to go on the warpath. That pounding rhythm in the bass evokes danger and crisis, action in the making. Perhaps Western-movie fans would be surprised to learn that the piece is the work of the man who composed such sweet and sentimental operetta confections as "Gypsy Love Song,"

Dagger Dance

from **Natoma**
Victor Herbert

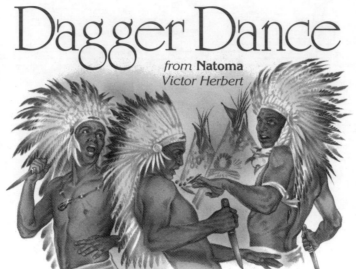

"Kiss Me Again" and "Thine Alone." But Victor Herbert was a man of many dimensions. Born in Dublin, Ireland, in 1859, he went from early fame as a cellist to far greater renown as a conductor and composer. Besides some 40 operettas, he wrote orchestral music and two grand operas. One opera, Natoma (1911), gave us the "Dagger Dance." The opera as a whole reflects the same interest in America and its native peoples that informs Antonín Dvořák's Ninth Symphony, From the New World, *written 20 years earlier.*

Maestoso (slowly and broadly)

N. C.*

Organ pedal may double lower note.

There are no real chords in this composition. The entire piece is built on the double pedal point D-A, which represents the tribal drums in the original score.

Coda

D.C. al Coda

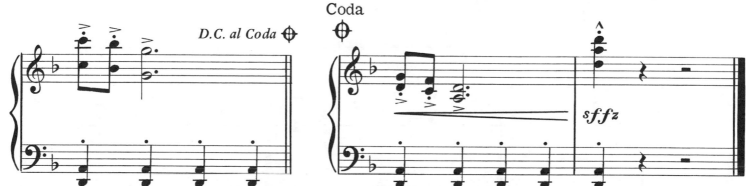

Indiana Jones March

John Williams
from **Raiders of the Lost Ark** and
Indiana Jones and the Temple of Doom

When Arthur Fiedler died in 1979, many assumed that no one, no matter how illustrious, could keep The Boston Pops Orchestra at the popularity level it had enjoyed throughout its many decades under Fiedler. Those people didn't count on the many-sided talents of John Williams. Already an acclaimed composer of film scores (The Poseidon Adventure, The Towering Inferno, Jaws), Williams was riding a new wave of success occasioned by his 1978 Academy Award for Star Wars when he was named conductor of The Pops in 1980. He immediately set to work reshaping the group in his image — with no loss of box-office appeal — and continued winning praise for his movie sound tracks. He wrote this lively and evocative march for the 1981 smash film hit Raiders of the Lost Ark, featuring Harrison Ford as the adventurer Indiana Jones. The theme proved so successful that Williams used it again in the Raiders sequel, Indiana Jones and the Temple of Doom. Not surprisingly, the march has recently become a staple of The Boston Pops' concert repertoire.

March tempo

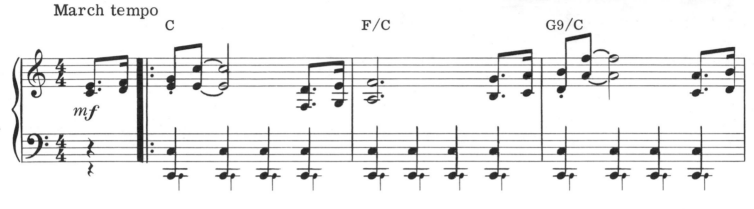

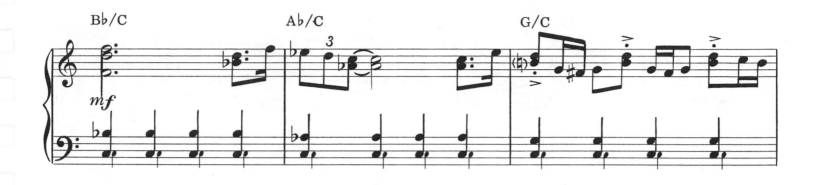

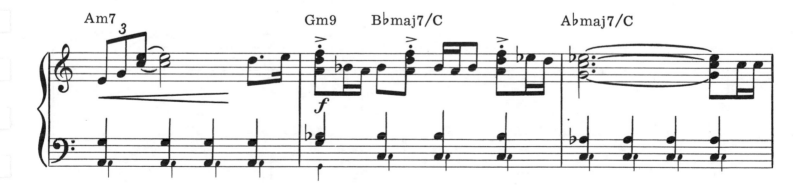

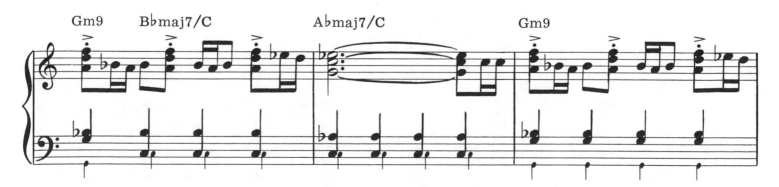

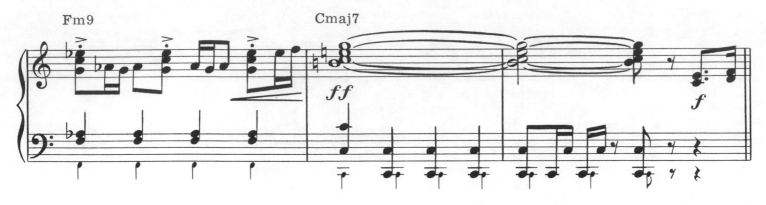

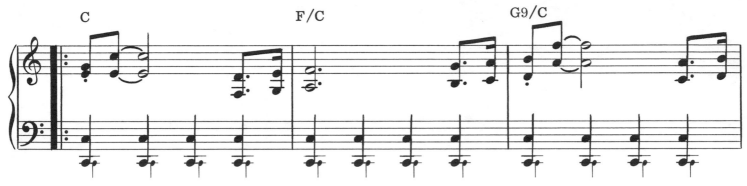

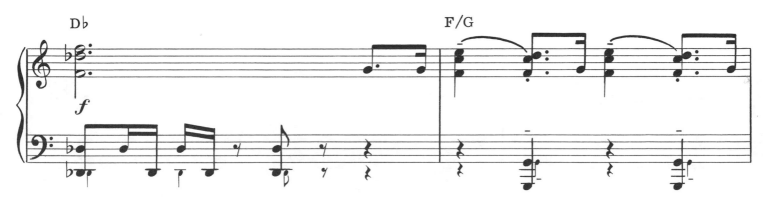

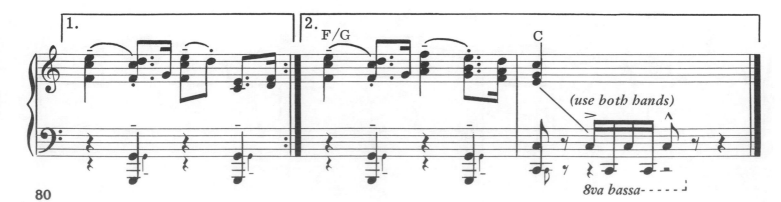

On the Trail

Ferde Grofé

from **Grand Canyon Suite**

and used on the **Philip Morris Radio Show**

Say there, all you old-time radio buffs. Remember Philip Morris's "Johnny" ... the little chap in the bellhop's uniform and cap back in the '40s (his full name was Johnny Roventini) who would turn up on the company-sponsored radio show, in magazine ads and even now and then in person, one hand cupped to his mouth, the other holding a pack of cigarettes as he exhorted all to "Call ... for ... Philip ... Mor-rees!"? Johnny's gone now, along with all the advertising slogans and so many of the products of that bygone era. But for those with long memories, it only takes a hearing of "On the Trail," the lazy, loping theme from Ferde Grofé's **Grand Canyon Suite,** *to bring it all back. For younger listeners, however, "On the Trail" is simply part of Grofé's colorful tone poem, with a donkey and rider, in silhouette, clop-clopping along the rim of the canyon just after sunrise.*

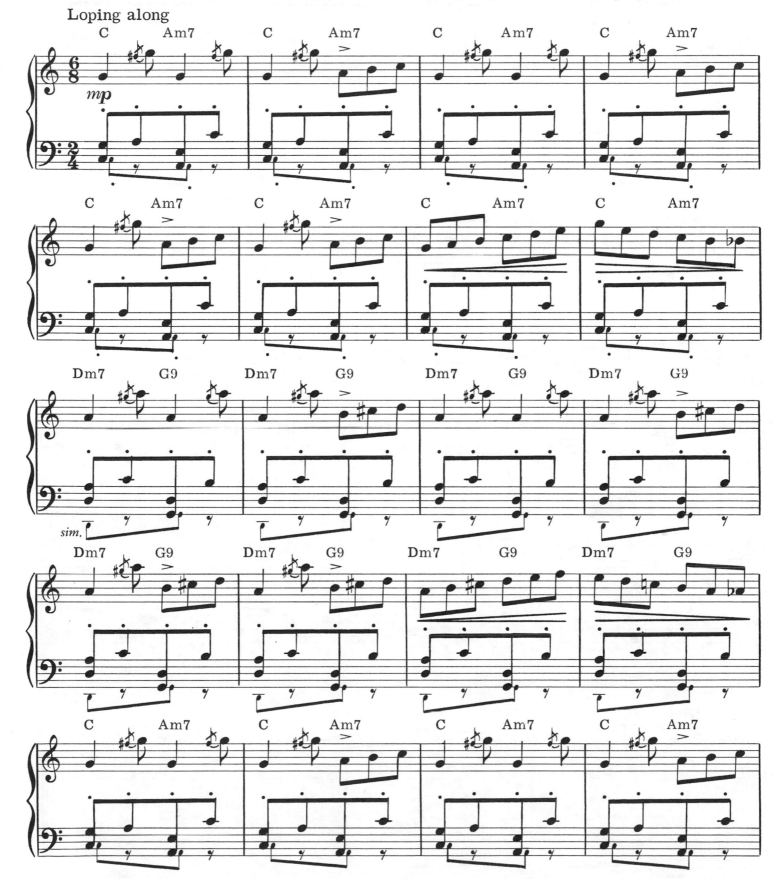

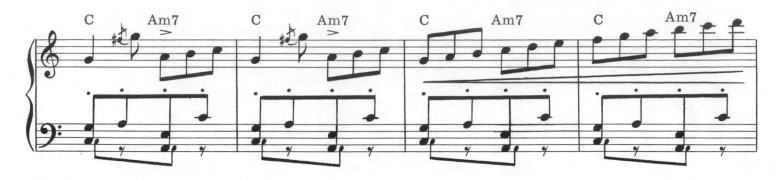

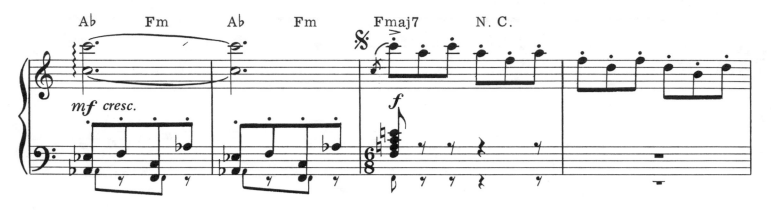

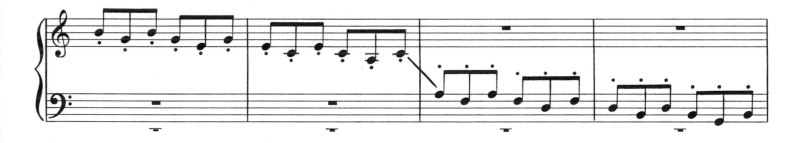

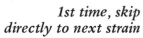

*1st time, skip
directly to next strain*

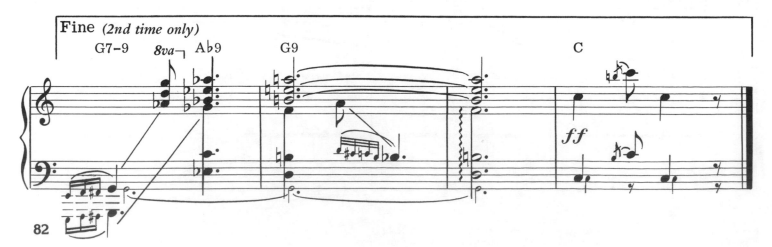

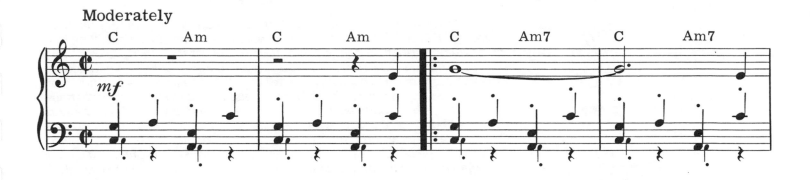

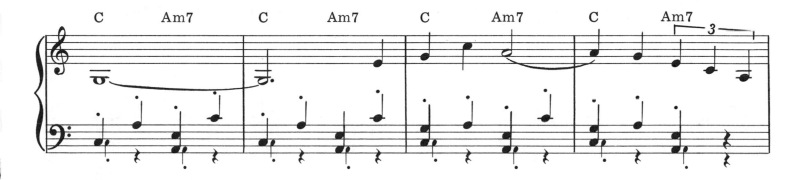

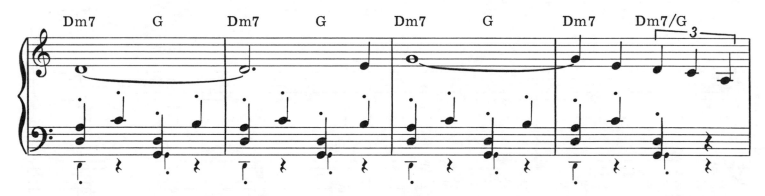

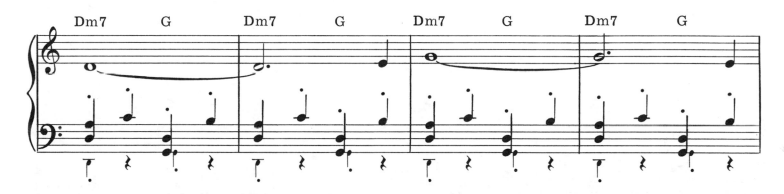

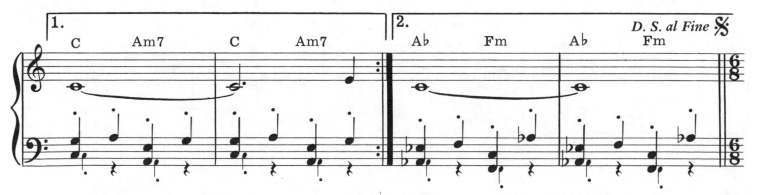

Johann Pachelbel
Used in **Ordinary People**

Radio and the movies can claim credit for having made a wide range of classical music familiar, even beloved, to a public that would never dream of setting foot inside a concert hall. For illustration, take several of the other pieces in this section of Popular Classics, or consider how many people know Giacomo Rossini's overture to his opera William Tell *only because it was theme music for* The Lone Ranger *on radio and TV. And how else would millions of people have known this small work by the rather obscure German composer Johann Pachelbel but for its use in TV commercials and most notably in the 1980 film* Ordinary People, *starring Mary Tyler Moore and Donald Sutherland? A gifted organist, Pachelbel was a friend of Johann Sebastian Bach's family and taught the organ to one of the future composer's brothers. His Canon in D, like much of his other work (almost all of it sacred music written for church use), is notable for its striking harmonic clarity and its melodic grace. The popularity of the piece has been enhanced greatly in recent years through a best-selling recording by flute virtuoso James Galway.*

Canon in D

Slow and sustained (♩=56)

*Note: 4 – bar chord progression and bass line repeat throughout the piece.

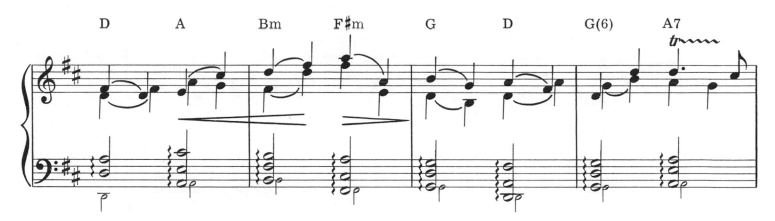

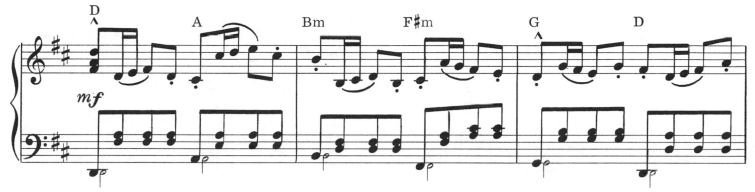

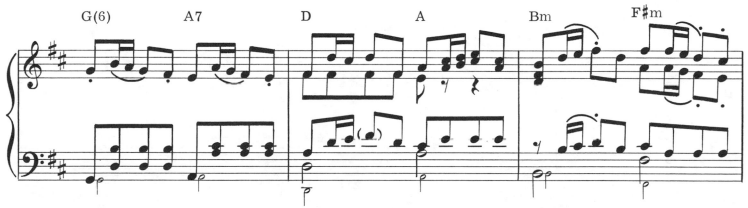

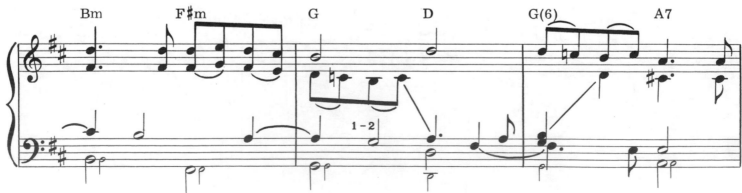

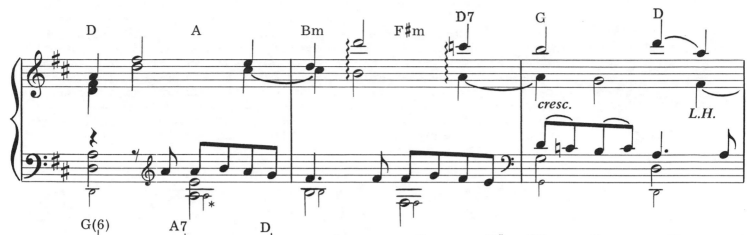

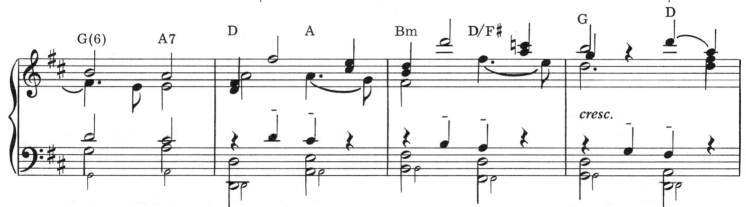

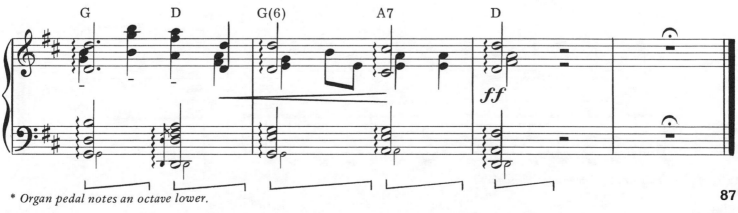

*Organ pedal notes an octave lower.

Spring

Antonio Vivaldi
Used in **The Four Seasons**

At first hearing, The Four Seasons *would seem an unlikely candidate for nomination as Vivaldi's — or any composer's — most popular work. But such thinking reckons without the pervasive and irresistible influence of television. Musically speaking, this set of four concertos for violin and orchestra, composed about 1720 and published five years later, is certainly charming. Originally, each section was preceded by a poem (penned, some scholars maintain, by Vivaldi himself) about the particular season. Each poem, in turn, was in three sections, corresponding to the traditional slow-fast-slow movement structure of the baroque concerto. "Spring" is the first of the sections and is as fresh and bright as the season it commemorates. It's not difficult, then, to understand why it has been used so frequently as background music for dozens of television commercials and in countless movies — including, appropriately, Alan Alda's* The Four Seasons *— usually as counterpoint to themes of young love, freedom, revitalization and renewal. It has been played in countless transcriptions and adaptations, including one for flute and orchestra that is performed frequently and effectively by flutist James Galway.*

Allegro

* Organ pedal may double lower note throughout.

Vivaldi: Mandolin Concerto

Antonio Vivaldi   Used in **Kramer vs. Kramer**

Meryl Streep

Dustin Hoffman

Son and protégé of a prominent Venetian violinist, Vivaldi studied for nearly a decade in a seminary, was ordained a priest while in his mid-20s and for most of his life held a post teaching music at a girls' school in Venice. He appeared widely throughout Europe as a concert violinist and left behind a remarkable quantity of music, including 500 concertos and as many as 50 operas. But beyond that, not much is known about him. As has happened to the works of so many prominent composers, his music fell into neglect after his death, lying forgotten until Italian scholars triggered a revival of interest in the early 1950s. His hitherto obscure concerto for mandolin, often played today as a solo piece for guitar, burst onto the classical "hit parade" after being used on the sound track of the 1979 film *Kramer vs. Kramer*, starring Dustin Hoffman and Meryl Streep. It joins The Four Seasons, four violin concertos written to accompany a set of sonnets describing the various times of the year, on the roster of Vivaldi's "greatest hits."

Allegro

* *Small bass notes for organ pedals or 3rd hand at the piano.*

Copyright © 1988 Ardee Music Publishing, Inc.

89

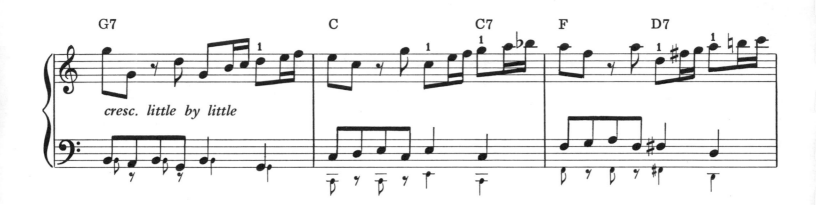

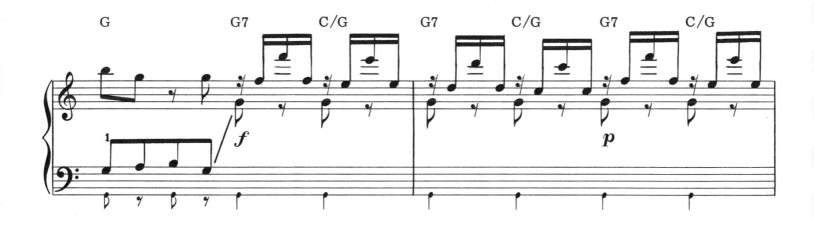

* Baroque trills begin on the note above the written note; this one played:

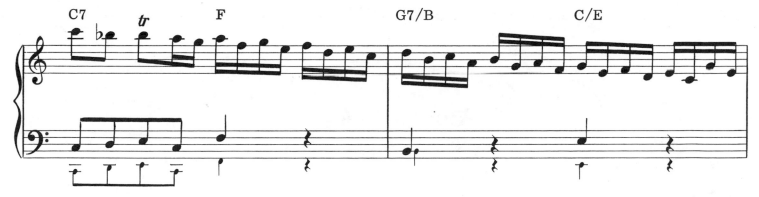

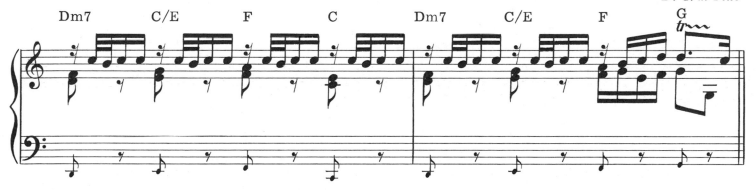

D. C. al Fine

4
Popular Classics with an American Accent

Duke Ellington

Mood Indigo

Duke Ellington, Barney Bigard and Irving Mills

The great "Duke" Ellington was always alert to thematic material that could be incorporated into a new composition. From the start, his bands were made up of star soloists who were often bursting with creative ideas of their own. Frequently, Ellington would pick up a phrase — perhaps one played by a band member during warmup, perhaps a musical thought worked out at rehearsal — and turn it into an instant classic. It is impossible to assess the full impact his great bandsmen had on the Ellington saga. "Mood Indigo," for example, began life in 1930 as "Dreamy Blues," based on a sketch by Ellington clarinetist Barney Bigard.

Indeed, the clarinet plays the major role in most performances of the tune. The piece is in two sections, chordally similar but melodically quite different, with the second section clearly a development of the first.

Belle of the Ball

Leroy Anderson

The dazzle of mid-19th-century Vienna, when an entire city seemed to whirl gaily to the waltzes of Johann Strauss, Jr., held lifelong fascination for Leroy Anderson. For him, the thought of a life of opulent royal balls in fairy-tale palaces and of wine, women and song in abundance was irresistible. It didn't matter to him that this image only applied to one small segment of the Austrian capital's population. As composers will, he expressed his obsession in music. Anderson's "Belle of the Ball" is a waltz full of the rich, swirling elegance of Strauss at his peak, and it

swept onto the music scene in 1953 to capture the imagination of the American popular-music world. It stayed on the charts for weeks, taking its place beside "Fiddle Faddle," "Sleigh Ride," "Blue Tango" and Anderson's other evocative and beloved musical miniatures. Anderson followed his hit with other triumphs. The former music tutor and college band director turned out "A Trumpeter's Lullaby," "The Bugler's Holiday," "The Syncopated Clock" and many other picturesque pieces that were popular in the years before rock and roll burst onto the pop-music scene.

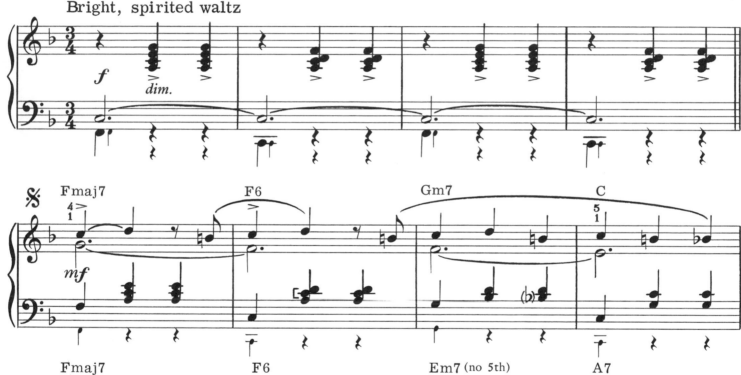

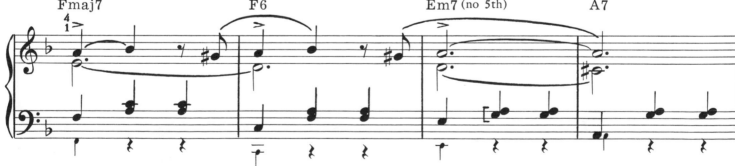

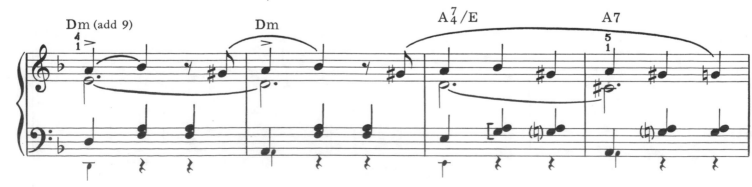

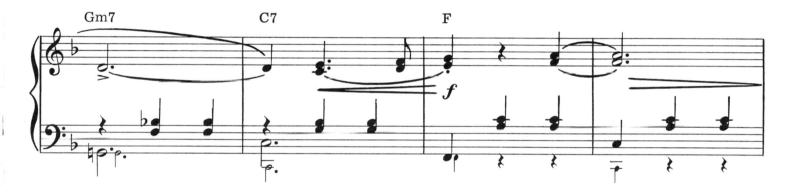

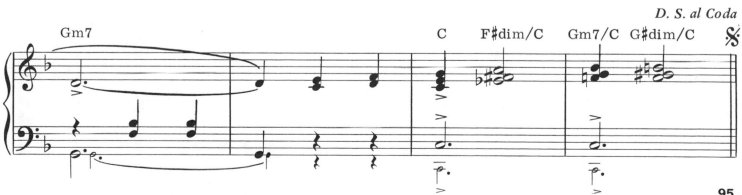

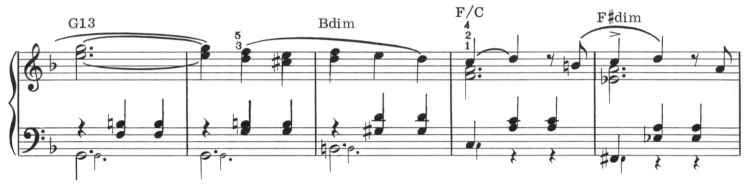

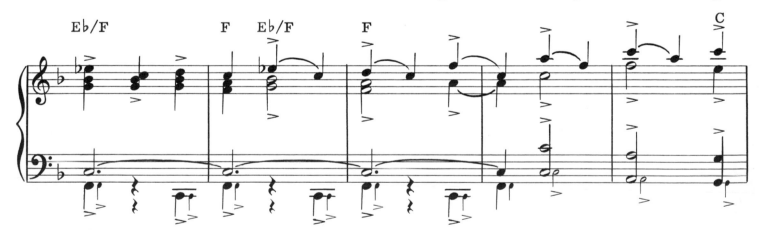

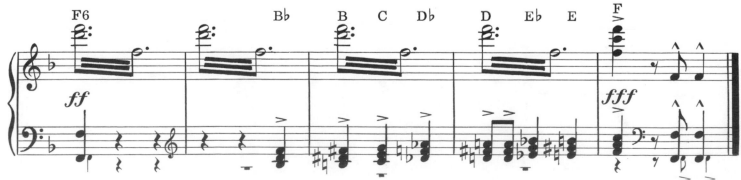

Many of the "modern" American concert works in the wave of Americana that sprang out of George Gershwin's success with "Rhapsody in Blue" celebrated New York City. There was, for just one example, Matty Malneck's "Park Avenue Fantasy" (which later became the popular song "Stairway to the Stars"). Much of the credit for this musical public relations effort for Manhattan goes to New York music publisher Jack Robbins, who actively encouraged such new works, especially those integrating jazz elements. Among the most lastingly successful pieces to emerge from Robbins' campaign was Louis Alter's "Manhattan Serenade." When he composed it in 1928, Alter was a struggling young pianist-songwriter from Massachusetts; his popular hits "You Turned the Tables on Me," "Do You Know What It Means to Miss New Orleans" and the rest still belonged to the future. Alter's Gotham portrait was so captivating a melody (Harold Adamson eventually added a lyric) that it turned up during the 1930s as the theme for Easy Aces, a popular radio series featuring humorist Goodman Ace and his wife, Jane — thereby entering a wider public consciousness than Alter could ever have anticipated.

Manhattan Serenade

Louis Alter

Lazy 4

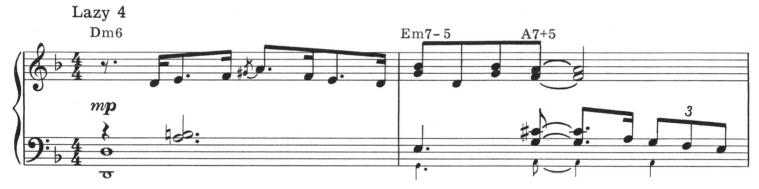

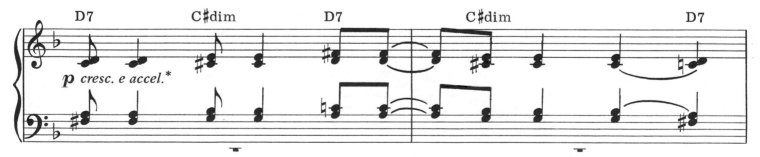

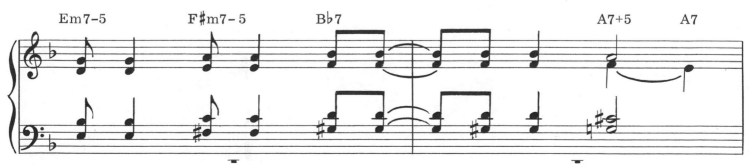

*Getting louder and faster.

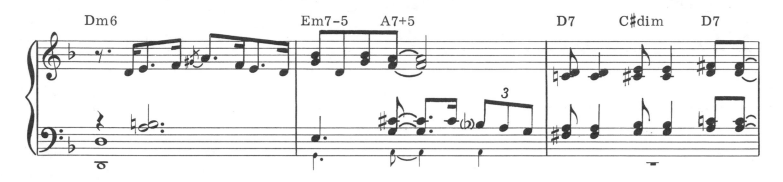

* Glissando on the white keys with the back of the third and fourth fingers and spear the Bb with the second finger à la Chico Marx.

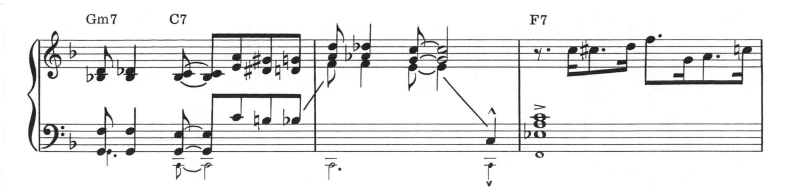

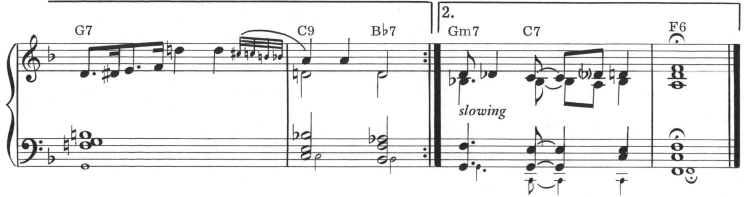

American Minuet
Harold Arlen

The echoes of George Gershwin's 1924 success with "Rhapsody in Blue" were still resounding throughout the American music world in the early 1940s. Convinced that the pathway to musical fame, riches and critical acclaim lay in jazz-accented concert pieces, most American composers tried their hands at it, encouraged and aided by farsighted publishers such as Jack Robbins. Flutist-composer Meredith Willson did his part by presenting a new short work by a different songwriter each week on his NBC radio show Good News. (Years later, Willson scored on Broadway with The Music Man.) Louis Alter, Vernon Duke, Peter De Rose, Duke Ellington, Ferde Grofé, Dana Suesse and Morton Gould were among the contributors — as was Harold Arlen. Arlen's "American Minuet," which he composed specifically for Good News, is sprightly and unpretentious. Though it's unlikely that the composer thought twice about the work after its debut on radio, "American Minuet" has survived, and several years ago, at a tribute to Arlen at Carnegie Hall, pianists Dick Hyman and Joe Bushkin played it as a duet — to enthusiastic audience response.

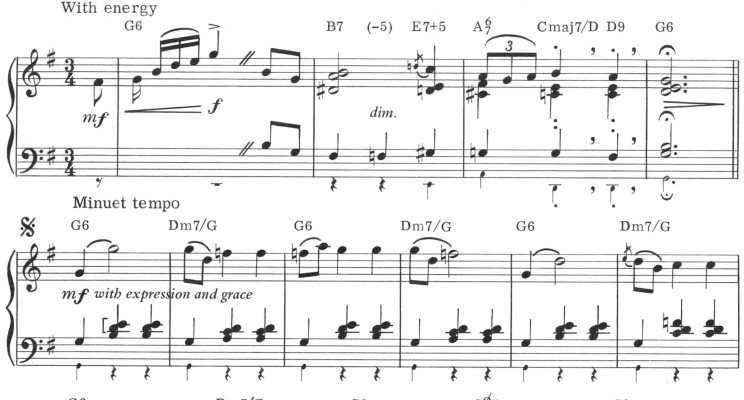

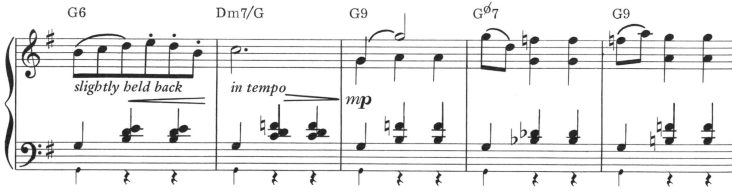

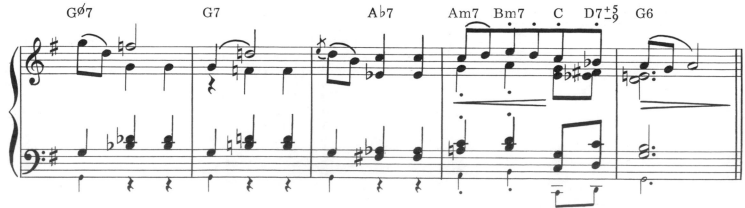

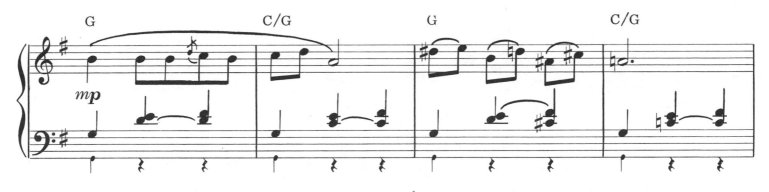

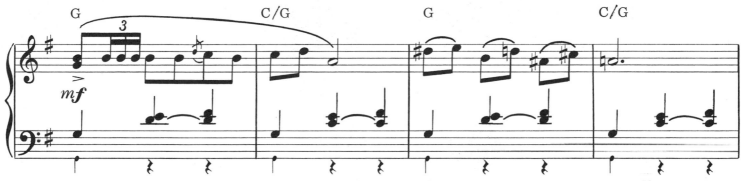

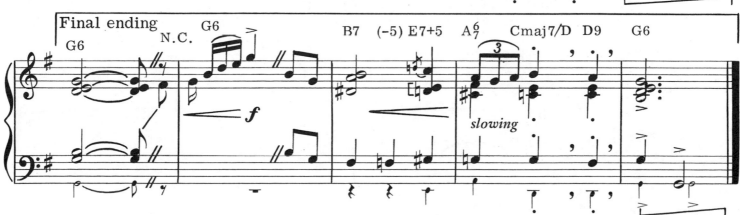

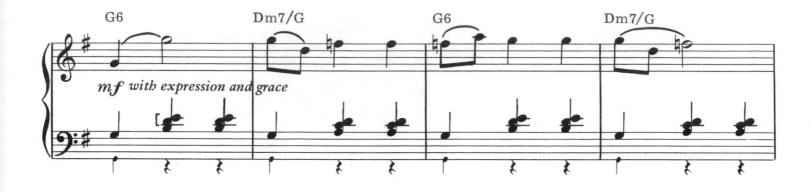

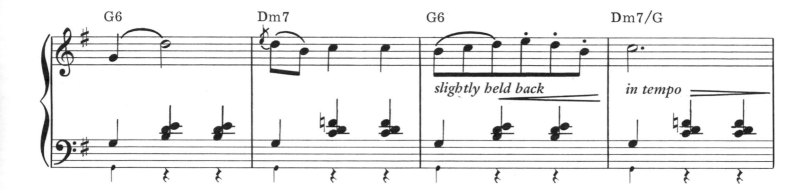

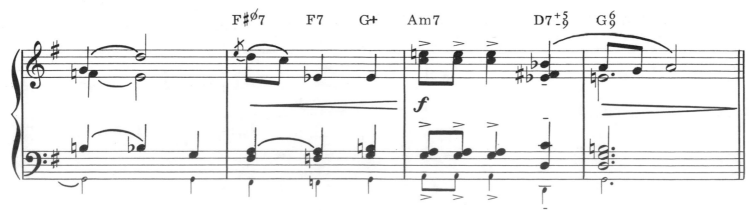

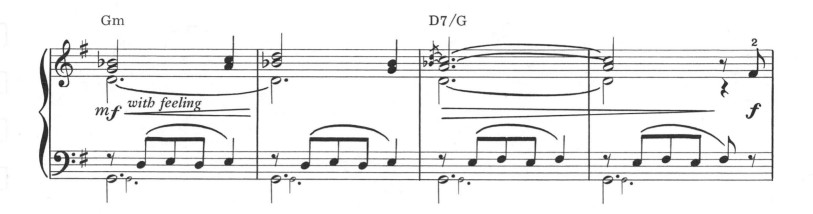

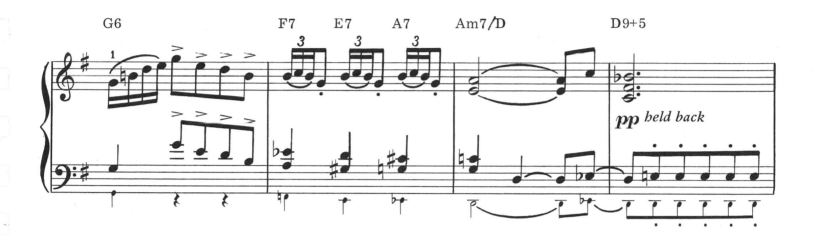

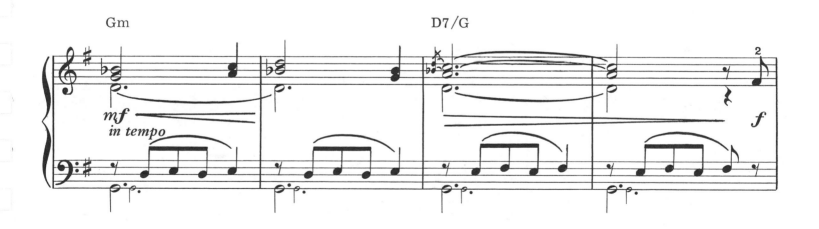

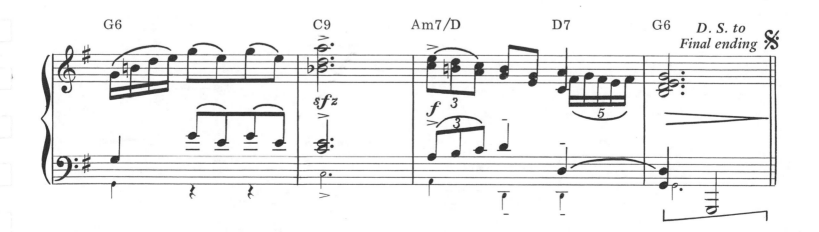

An American in Paris - Blues Theme

George Gershwin

Between George Gershwin's first visit to Paris, in 1923, and his return to the French capital five years later, much had happened. "Rhapsody in Blue" had established Gershwin as a musical double threat, equally respected in the separate worlds of the Broadway stage and the concert hall. His Concerto in F had simply reinforced this reputation. The composer was now a celebrity. As his biographer Charles Schwartz later wrote, "Like a royal potentate, Gershwin could sit back and wait to be sought out. In Paris, as elsewhere, he was in great demand." That meant, among other things, visits from such musical legends as fellow-composers Sergei Prokofiev, Darius Milhaud, William Walton, Francis Poulenc and Maurice Ravel. It meant an especially warm tête-à-tête with the celebrated composition teacher Nadia Boulanger, who taught Aaron Copland and many other aspiring young Americans. While staying in Paris at the luxurious Majestic Hotel, Gershwin worked on the concert piece "An American in Paris." He completed the famous blues section there, presumably in between visits with his illustrious colleagues.

Not too fast, but with a strong beat

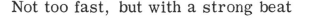

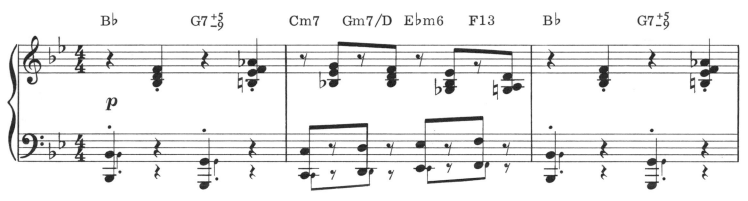

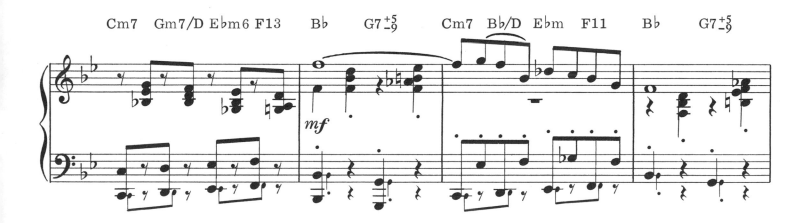

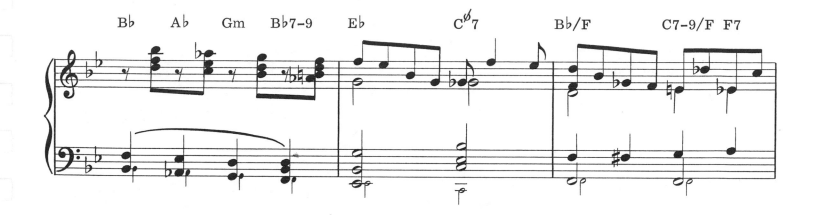

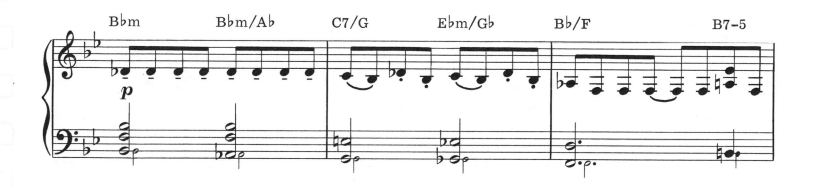

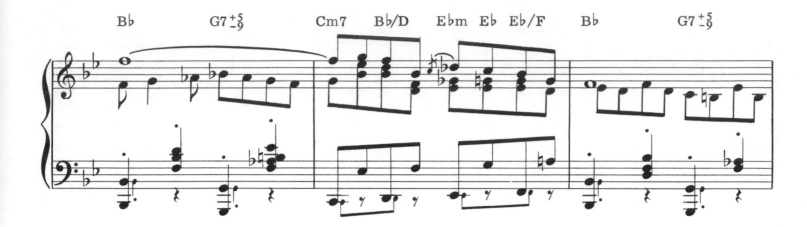

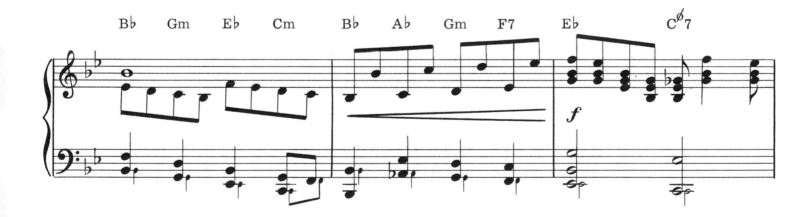

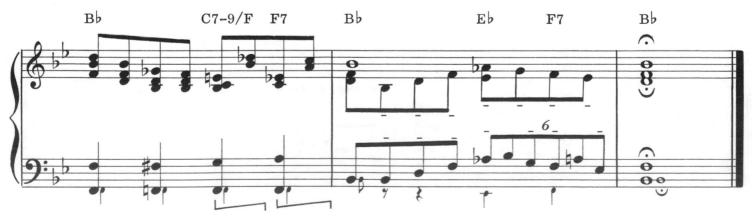

Yesterthoughts

Victor Herbert

By the end of the 1930s, Victor Herbert's popularity, once enormous, had become a thing of the past. The great industrialist-philanthropist Andrew Carnegie once said, "My idea of heaven is to be able to sit and listen to all the music by Victor Herbert that I want to." Now he and Herbert and the world they had known were dust. But Herbert's music lived on. In 1940 — nearly 20 years after the composer's death and 40 years after this lovely work was first published — "Yesterthoughts" finally attracted the attention it deserved, though in a form that would have seemed amusing to Herbert himself. For it was only when lyrics were added by Stanley Adams and a big band adopted the song that it became popular. The band was none other than Glenn Miller's. The song, featuring vocalist Ray Eberle, was recorded, and though never an out-and-out smash, it did become a favorite with Miller's audience, few of whom were old enough to be familiar with Herbert's work.

Street Scene
Alfred Newman

"They all wanted to be Gershwin" is pianist Dick Wellstood's way of describing the efforts of composers in the late 1920s and early '30s — from Fats Waller to Bix Beiderbecke to Louis Alter — to write concert works in the style of "Rhapsody in Blue." George Gershwin was indeed the man of the hour — glamorous, successful and, perhaps most important, respected in both the popular and "serious" music worlds. Among the new works released at the time by publisher Jack Robbins was Alfred Newman's score for the Hollywood adaptation of Elmer Rice's 1929 Pulitzer Prize-winning play Street Scene. *The resultant attention and critical acclaim won Newman a secure place among film composers. The major theme of Newman's treatment, arranged here, acquired a Harold Adamson lyric in 1942 and surfaced as "Sentimental Rhapsody." In 1953, the long prologue to the Marilyn Monroe film* How to Marry a Millionaire *featured Newman directing a large studio orchestra that was playing his original* Street Scene *music. And* Street Scene *had a continued life of its own, too: A new production, this one with memorable music by Kurt Weill, ran on Broadway in 1947.*

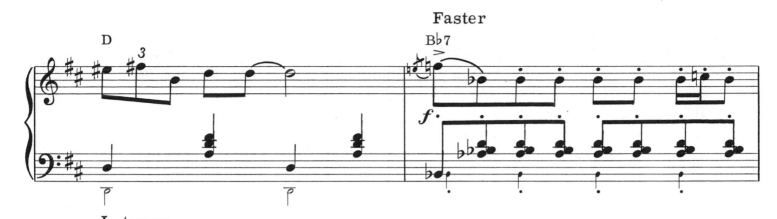

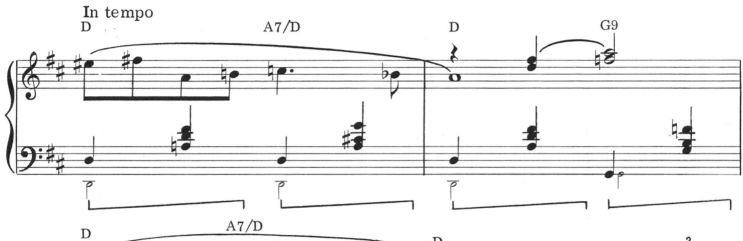

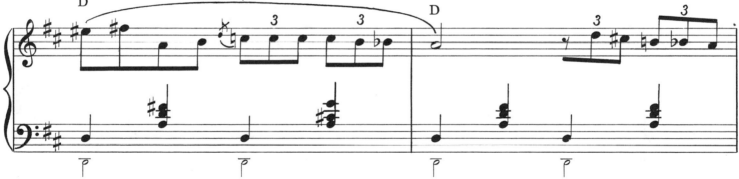

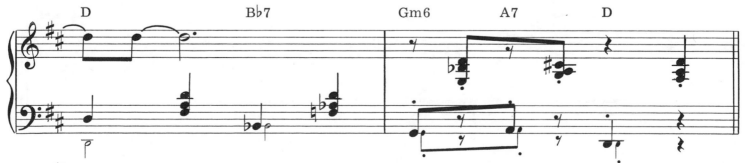

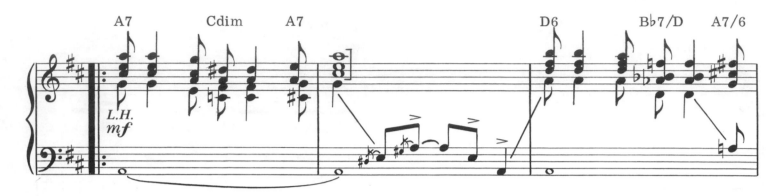

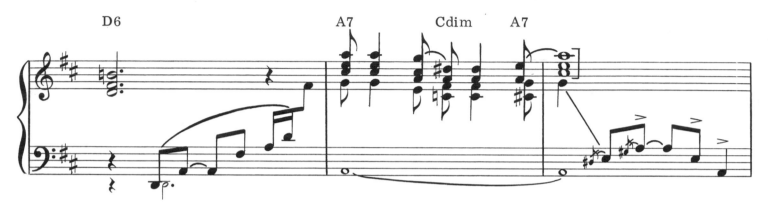

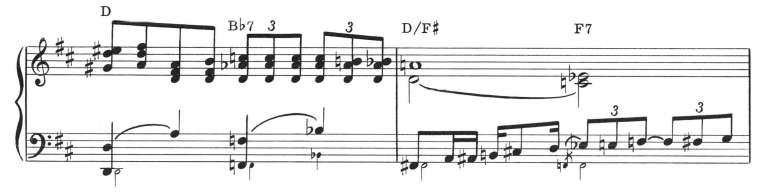

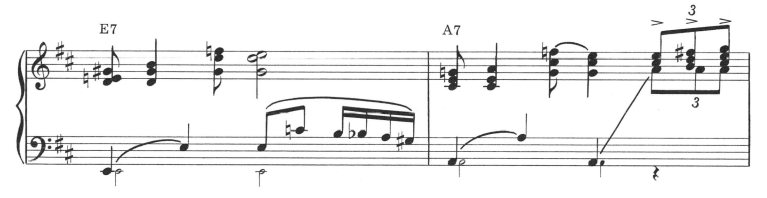

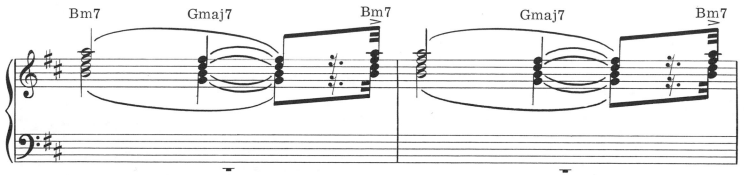

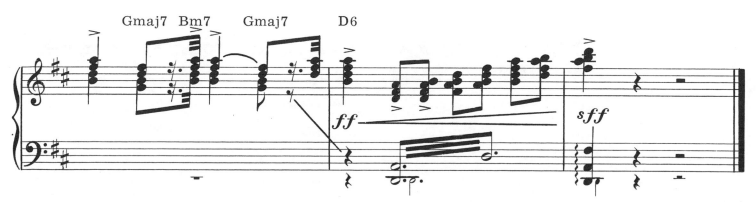

One-Note Rag

Dan Fox

Dan Fox

The following appears on the title page of several of Scott Joplin's classic rags: "Notice: Do not play this piece fast. It is never right to play 'ragtime' fast." The ragtime revival of the 1970s, in particular the record albums and concert appearances of pianist-musicologist Joshua Rifkin, underscored Joplin's admonition. Ragtime was not just for fun; it was serious music to be played with care and skill. And it wasn't jazz. There are no alterations or thematic improvisations; the notes are to be played as written. The ragtime boom, helped no end by Marvin Hamlisch's use of Joplin's "The Entertainer" in the film The Sting, came and went — leaving a lasting public recognition and appreciation of classic ragtime. Our arranger Dan Fox's "One-Note Rag" is new, but it obviously belongs to the idiom's compositional tradition, as carried on by such other masters as Max Morath, Dick Hyman and William Bolcom. The main theme of Dan's piece is a play on a single note but within a world of subtle variation that is rewarding — and great fun — for any pianist.

Not too fast

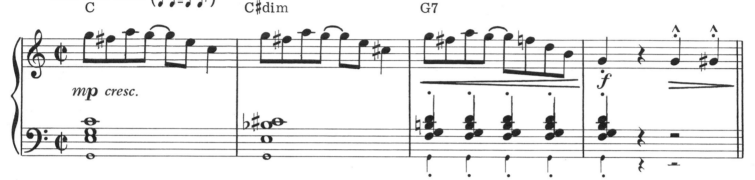

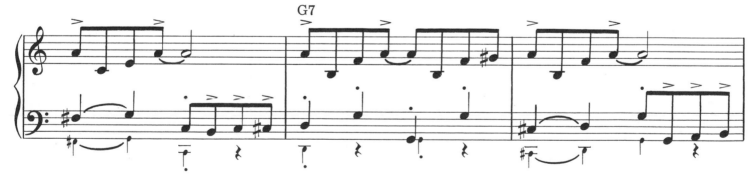

114

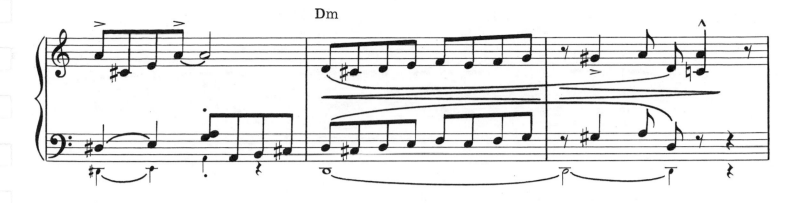

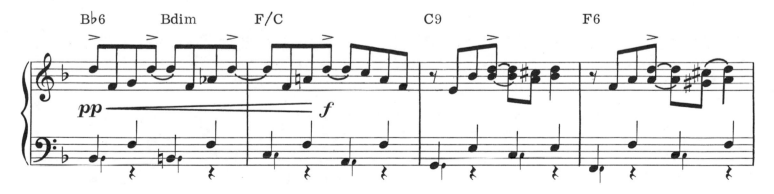

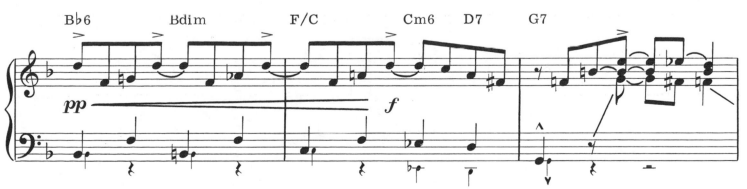

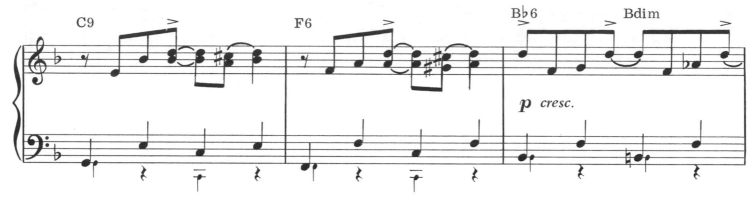

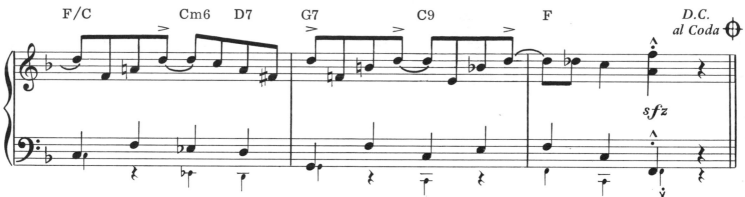

Although Wolfgang Amadeus Mozart died at the early age of 35, he brought forth more great and enduring music than most other composers could create in twice the time span. His last three symphonies, for example, were composed, in 1788, in the space of only seven weeks. Fellow composer Robert Schumann particularly admired the "grace and charm" of the Symphony in G Minor, known as No. 40. His words were occasioned, no

5
Unforgettable Themes from Popular Symphonies

doubt, by the quiet elegance of the opening-movement theme, which is arranged here. At the time, Mozart was living in Vienna — "a splendid place," he wrote his father — but ill health, constant lack of money, a spendthrift wife and inability to write down all the music teeming in his brain often made the days a torment. None of this turmoil permeates the music, however. In its grace and humanity, the music has never been surpassed.

Mozart: Symphony No. 40 in G Minor
First Movement Theme
Wolfgang Amadeus Mozart

Mozart: *Symphony No. 40 (First Movement Theme)*

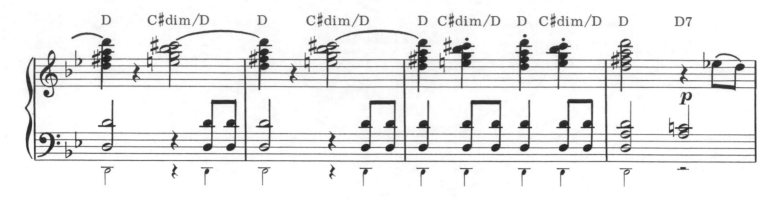

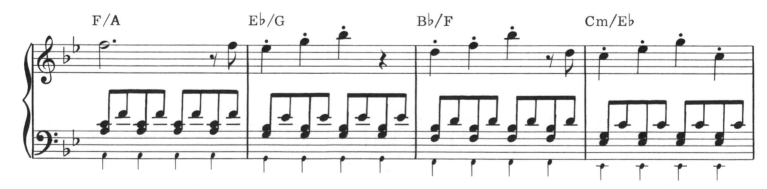

Easier:

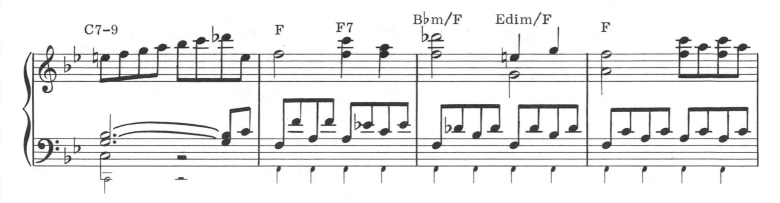

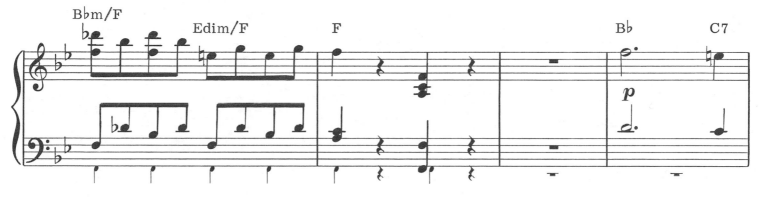

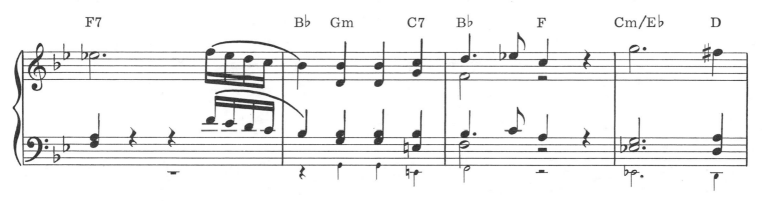

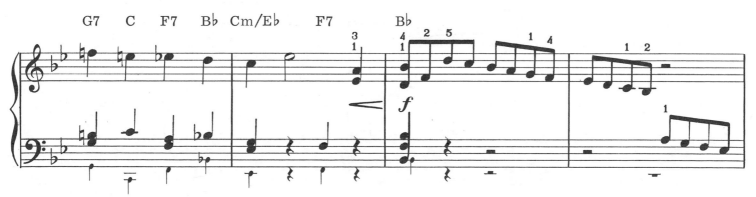

Dvorak: "New World" Symphony
Second Movement—Largo

Antonín Dvořák

Dvořák was 51 years old when a wealthy American admirer, Jeanette H. Thurber, invited him to New York City to direct her National Conservatory of Music. Of all "nationalist" composers, she felt that the Czech Dvořák was the most outstanding, and she was very determined to establish the

conservatory as a haven for American composers wherein they could write "American" music. Dvořák arrived with his family to spend a happy three years, teaching and conducting. In the summers, he moved to a Czech community in Iowa, where he acted as church organist and also created some of his finest scores, such as his ninth and final symphony, From the New World. Although Dvořák was very interested in indigenous American music, he never used it in his own works. Rather, he tried to interpret the idiom of America in his own way. This Largo from the ninth symphony's second movement is totally Dvořák, not a Negro spiritual as many have suggested. (The words of the song "Goin' Home" were added later.) The melody is so evocative of a poignant melancholy that it was used to project that feeling in The Snake Pit, a 1947 film starring Olivia de Havilland as a helpless patient in a demoralizing mental clinic.

Beethoven: Symphony No. 3 ("Eroica")

Ludwig van Beethoven

Fourth Movement–Country Dance

In 1803, a year after Beethoven discovered that he would eventually be completely deaf, he summoned all his creative powers to write a symphony that would change the course of music in its affirmation of faith. His Third Symphony bears the name "Eroica" ("Heroic") because Beethoven had intended to dedicate it to Napoleon, a sworn republican, as was the composer. However, when the little Corsican changed his politics and became Emperor, Beethoven recoiled.

He angrily destroyed the original dedication and simply called his Heroic Symphony "the celebration of the memory of a great man." For a finale to the symphony, he wrote a set of variations on a theme he had composed two years earlier — and used twice since then — for a ballet about Prometheus, the mythic figure who gave the gods' gift of fire to man. One of the variations is this "Country Dance," which he grouped together in a set of pieces called "Country Dances."

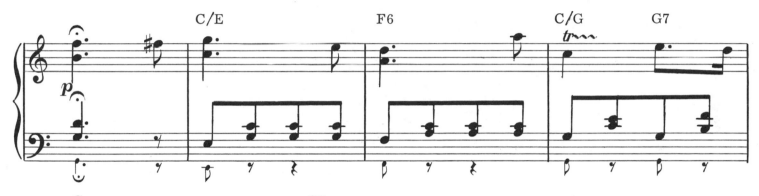

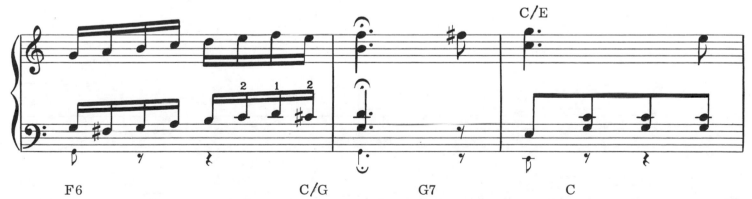

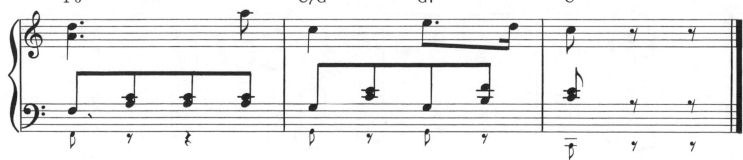

Brahms: Symphony No.1 Fourth Movement Theme

Johannes Brahms

Johannes Brahms waited a long time before he published his First Symphony — he had just turned 44 when he put the final touches to it. Perhaps he was apprehensive about being compared to his idol Beethoven, whose immortal nine were the standard by which all others were judged. Brahms, in fact, had thrown several attempts away, and he had been nearly 22 years at work on this Symphony in C Minor before it satisfied him. When the work finally made its way into the world, it was generally lauded. But Brahms, as usual, was unsure of its quality. In his modest but gruff way, he scoffed at a fellow musician who extolled it as "Beethoven's Tenth" and agreed with those who found Beethoven's influence too

strong, particularly in the final movement, which is excerpted here. The main theme is one of the most beautiful melodies ever created, with the compelling energy of a rallying cry and the surging poetry of a great hymn. Those who, perhaps out of envy, pretended to find evidence that Brahms had filched musical motifs quickly told him that this theme reminded them of the "Ode to Joy" of Beethoven's Ninth Symphony, written half a century earlier. "Every donkey hears that," Brahms is supposed to have said, perhaps meaning that one has to be a donkey to hear it. For us, now, it remains one of the great themes of music, something only Brahms could have written.

Allegro non troppo, ma con brio (not too fast, but with spirit)

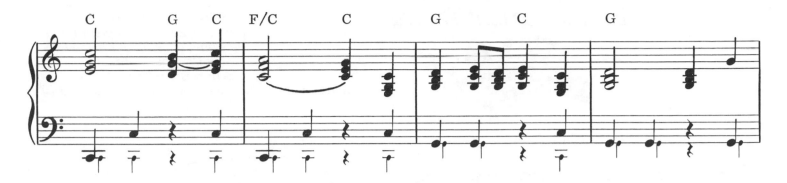

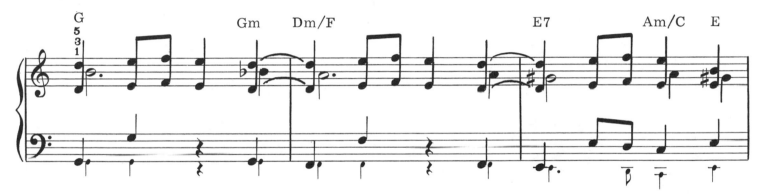

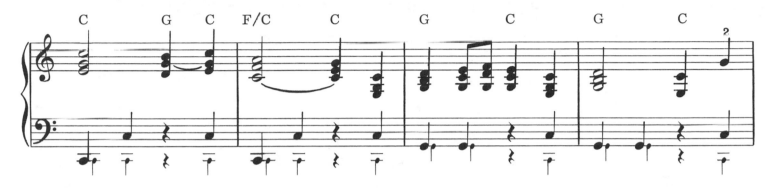

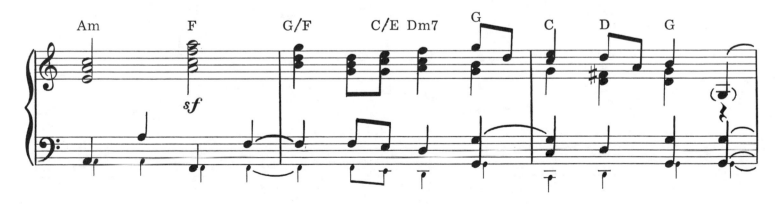

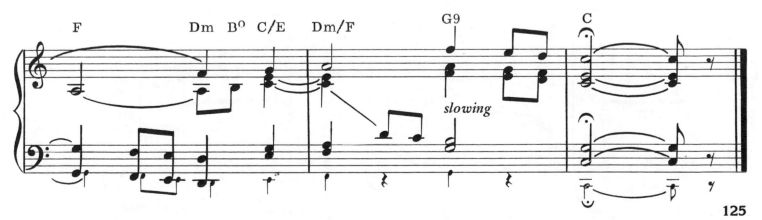

Brahms: Symphony No. 2
First Movement Theme

Johannes Brahms

Robert Schumann was clearly excited. "Come here," he called out to his pianist wife Clara, "and you'll hear music unlike any you've ever heard before." The cause of Schumann's excitement was a broodingly intense 20-year-old pianist from the slums of Hamburg named Johannes Brahms. Brahms had come to Schumann with a letter of introduction from the eminent violinist

Allegro ma non troppo (not too fast)

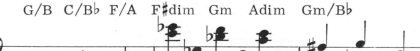

Brahms: Symphony No. 4
First Movement Theme

Johannes Brahms

By the time Brahms was ready to write his fourth and last symphony, he was at the height of his powers and his fame. He had lived for many years in Vienna and had become an institution in the city, beloved of its citizens, honored by its musicians. His place in history was assured. But, always, his confidence in any major new work he was composing was quavery. Of the new symphony, he wrote to one friend only half-jokingly, "My latest attack was evidently a complete failure. A symphony too!" To another he wrote, "I haven't the ghost of an idea whether I shall let the thing be printed." And to still another, comparing his symphony to an orchard, "But around here the cherries are not sweet and eatable." But the first performance of the symphony was a huge success. One of his most esteemed "critics" wrote to him: "It is a walk through exquisite scenery at sunset, when the colors deepen and the crimson grows to purple." This theme from the first movement, with the simplicity of genius, seems like a muted dance filled with easy leaps and graceful swirls, accompanied by rising arpeggios in the bass. (The second-movement theme begins on page 130.) Vienna continued to applaud the Fourth Symphony, and it was programmed frequently, including one particularly memorable occasion during the last year of Brahms' life. By then he was terribly ill with cancer of the liver. The Viennese knew it, and their hearts went out to him. The performance was received with wild enthusiasm. When the frail composer stood to receive the audience's plaudits and its shouts of affection, many in the theater were reduced to tears.

Very moderately

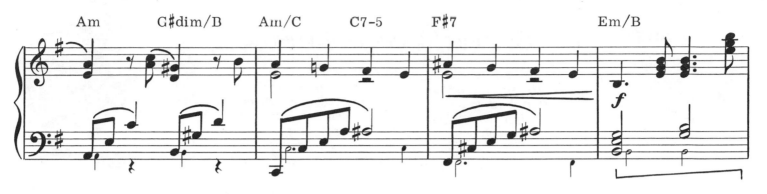

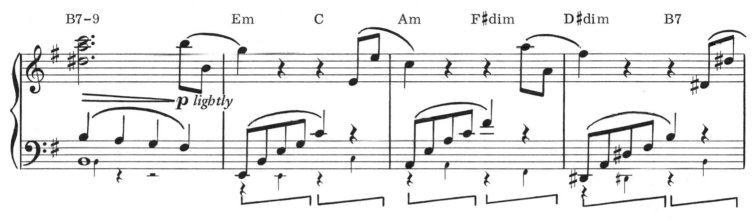

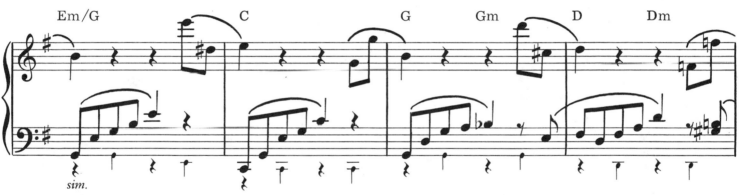

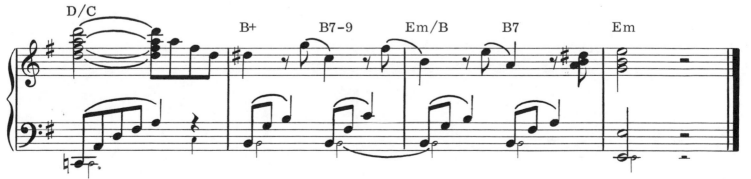

Brahms: Symphony No. 4
Second Movement Theme

Johannes Brahms

The second-movement theme of Brahms' Symphony No. 4 (turn back to page 128 for the first-movement theme) is filled with melancholy yet buttressed with strength, resembling a slow march in 3/4 time. The same rhythmic figure is repeated until the ending, with its upwardly floating, richly textured harmonic line that leads to an elemental C major chord.

Andante moderato (not fast)

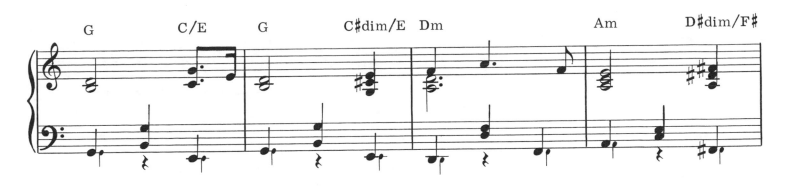

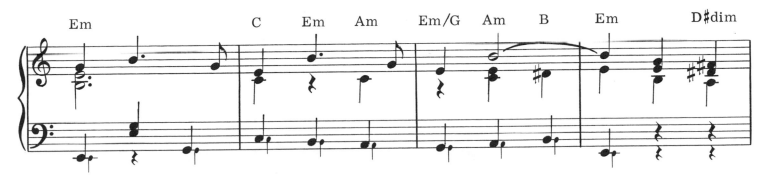

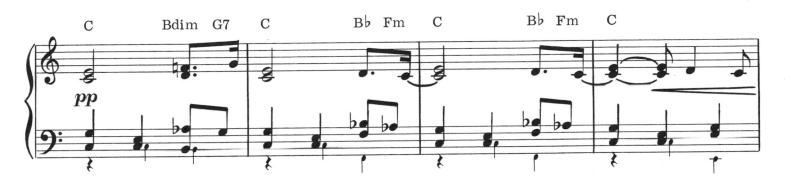

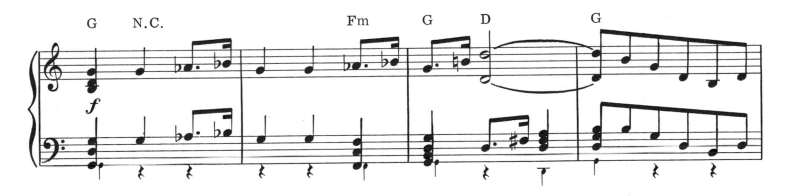

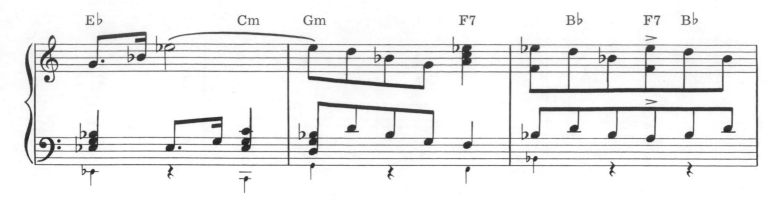

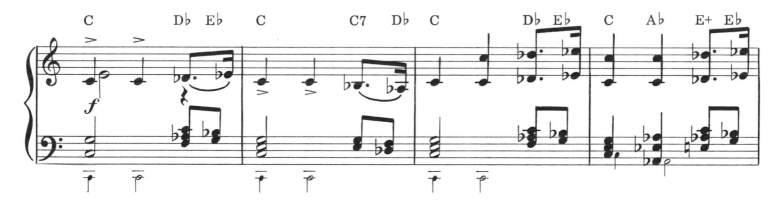

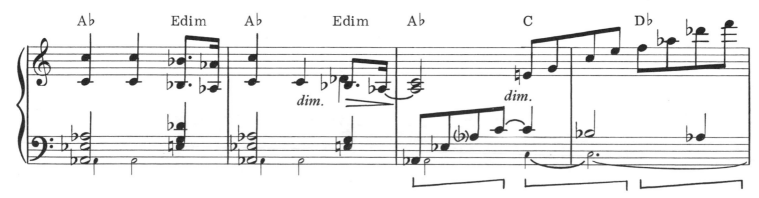

Beethoven: Symphony No. 6 ("Pastoral")

First Movement – Awakening of cheerful emotions on arriving in the country

Ludwig van Beethoven

"A recollection of country life ... a pastoral symphony ... emotions aroused by the pleasure of the country" — these phrases from Beethoven's sketchbooks were written at about the time that he was working on the "Pastoral" Symphony, probably the first truly great piece of programmatic music (music that tells a definite story). "Awakening of cheerful emotions on arriving in the country" was the way he finally labeled the first movement in the score, published in 1809. Then comes an idyll by the brook, followed by a scene of shepherds merrymaking. A thunderstorm breaks into their dance, but when it subsides the shepherds gather again to sing a hymn of their thankfulness after the storm (see page 136). By the time Beethoven wrote the "Pastoral," he had become inured to the deafness that assailed him. His descriptive composition came solely from what he remembered. While walking in the Wienerwald, near where he had written it, he told his companion, "It was here that I composed the 'Scene at the Brook,' and the yellowhammers, quails, nightingales and cuckoos up there composed along with me."

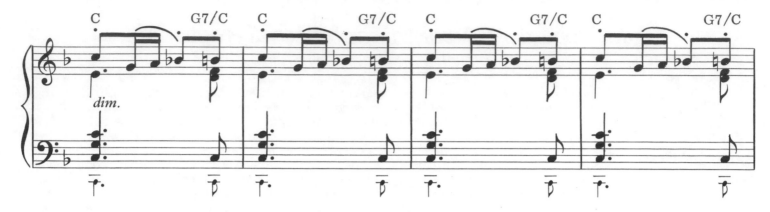

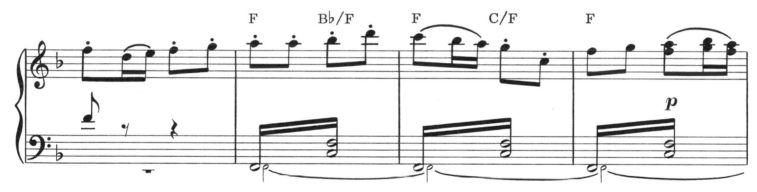

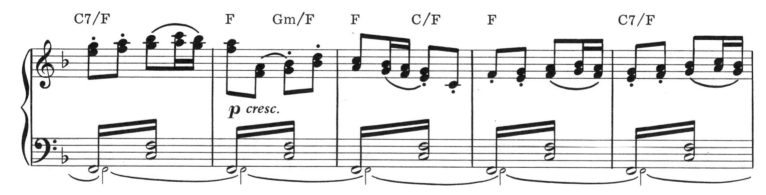

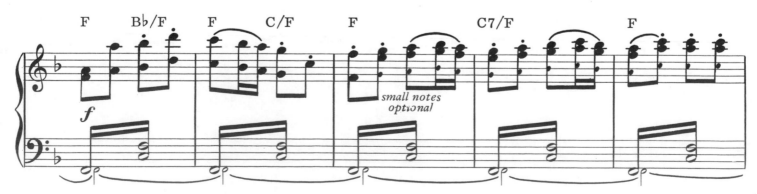

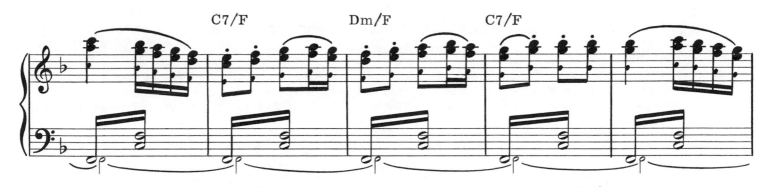

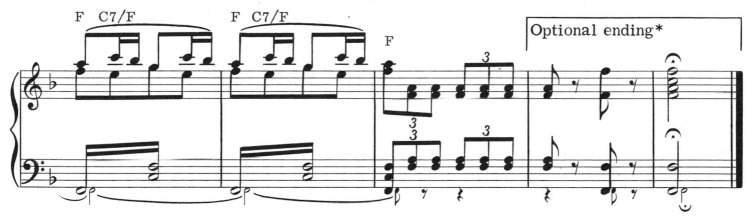

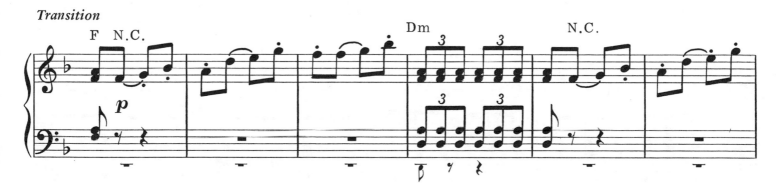

Use these two bars as an ending only if you wish to bring the piece to a complete close. We suggest, however, skipping them and using the next section (marked Transition) to get to the next selection, "Shepherd's Song," from this symphony.

Beethoven: Symphony No.6 ("Pastoral")

Final Movement-Shepherd's Song

Ludwig van Beethoven

This excerpt from Beethoven's Symphony No. 6, which is titled "Shepherd's Song," is the beginning of the final movement, after the shepherds who have been routed by the storm reassemble in the meadows. The skies clear, the sun once more warms the fields, and the shepherds sing their quiet hymn of gratitude.

Allegretto, in 2 (each ♩.=1 slow beat)

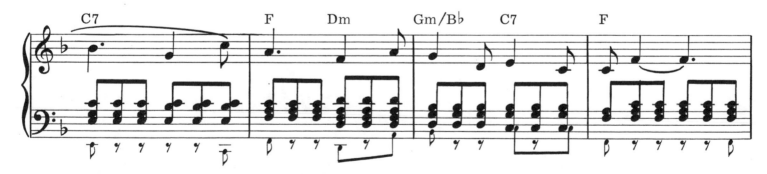

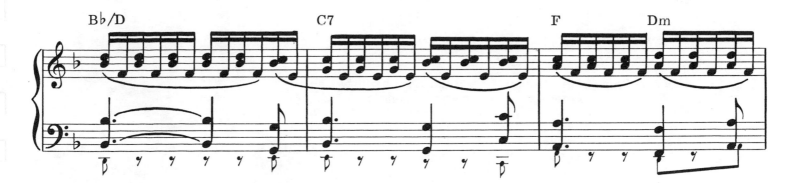

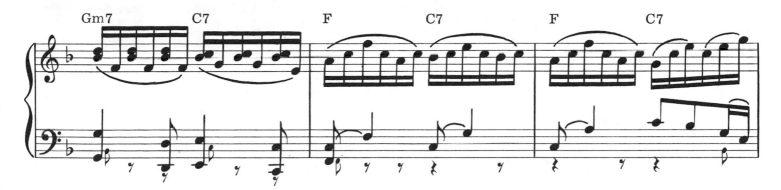

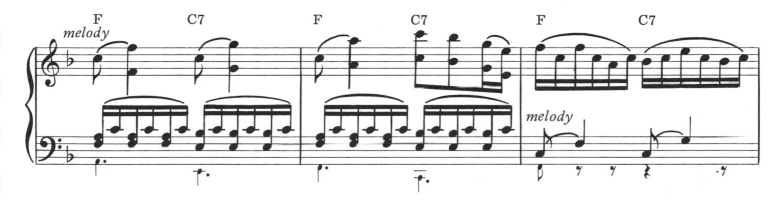

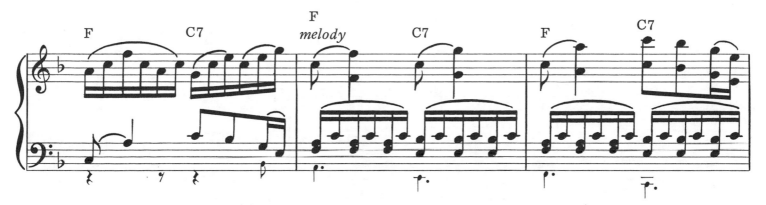

Beethoven: Symphony No. 7
Second Movement Theme
Ludwig van Beethoven

Each of the four movements in Beethoven's Seventh Symphony has an almost balletic feeling. This is true even of the majestic second movement, which, like some sumptuous saraband, moves at a more dignified but steady beat. Once begun, the rhythm does not change — one long note followed by two shorter ones and then two long ones again before the pattern repeats itself. Not content with one haunting melody, Beethoven gives us another simultaneously — beginning here with the final two measures of line 4, heard in the lower voice of the right hand: C, B, B-C-D and so on. When Beethoven was a young composer, Mozart sent him a tune to improvise on, including as a joke a double theme like this one. The idea must have amused Beethoven, and almost 40 years later he repeated the feat in this symphony.

*Pianists: Play L.H. 8va lower till ***

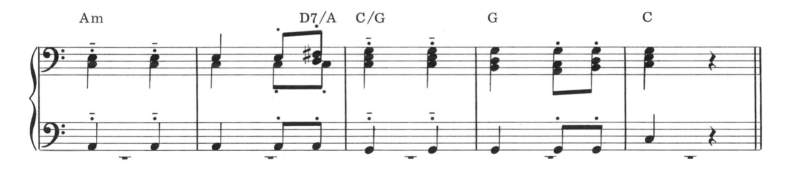

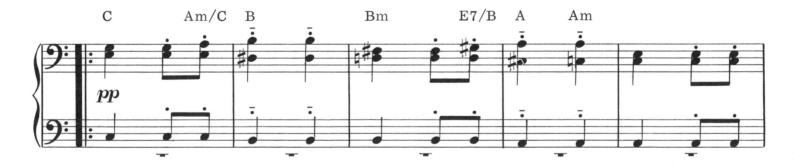

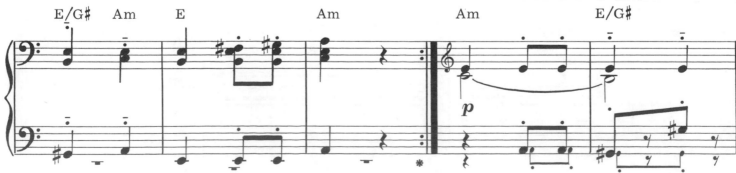

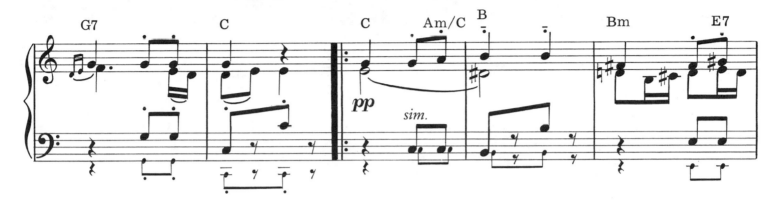

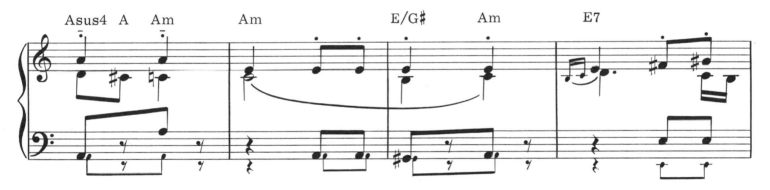

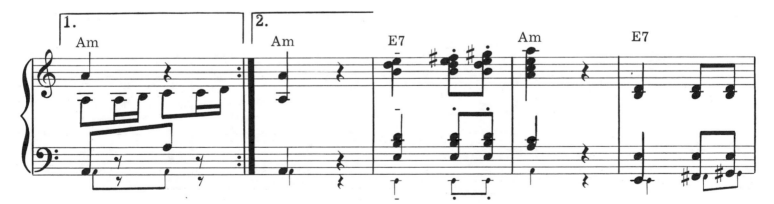

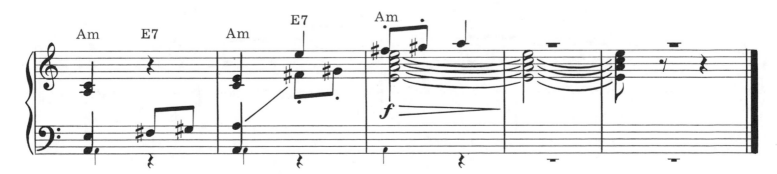

Haydn: "Surprise" Symphony
Second Movement Theme
Franz Joseph Haydn

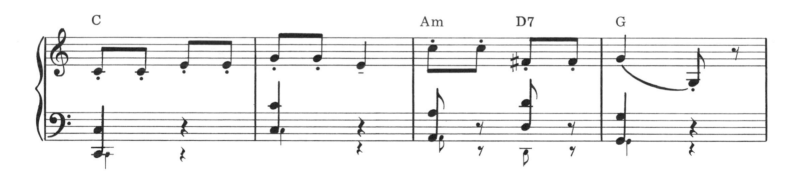

In the later years of his incredibly productive life, Franz Joseph Haydn was invited to visit London by the German-born impresario-violinist Johann Peter Salomon, who secured at the same time Haydn's promise to write six symphonies for a series of subscription concerts. Haydn's visit was a splendid success. He was already known and admired in England and as a result was invited everywhere, including royal concerts (he was overwhelmed when he heard Handel's "Hallelujah" Chorus). He gave music lessons to many young women and received an honorary doctorate from Oxford University. Salomon's subscription concerts were played to enthusiastic audiences, with receipts nearly double what had been estimated. The programs were generally made up of concertos, instrumental solos or vocal works, but each included one or two Haydn symphonies. Salomon continued the concerts for a number of years, long after Haydn himself had returned to Vienna. They became very popular and spread Haydn's name throughout musical circles. H. C. Robbins Landon, Haydn's biographer, writes that Haydn was the first composer in the history of music to become truly famous throughout Europe in his lifetime. The so-called "Surprise" Symphony, written in 1791, the year Haydn arrived in London, derives part of its popularity from the second movement, with its "surprise" — the violins in the original play a childlike little tune in staccato notes, repeating it even more quietly until at the end the entire orchestra punctuates it with a fortissimo chord. Stories had it that the first audiences were so flabbergasted by the sudden chord that they began to giggle and when it was repeated broke into guffaws. Although such stories are probably apocryphal, the "Surprise" nickname has remained. What also remains is the delicacy and winsomeness of Haydn at his best. He ultimately wrote 12 symphonies for Salomon — the "Surprise" was the second — and the money he earned in England allowed him to return to Vienna and live the rest of his life in comparative luxury.

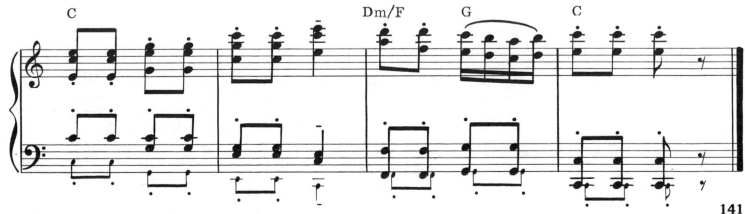

Mahler: Symphony No. 1

Gustav Mahler

Third Movement – "Frère Jacques" Theme

For the somewhat lugubrious third-movement theme from his Symphony No. 1, excerpted here, Gustav Mahler used the old French tune "Frère Jacques," but in a minor mode. The melody is a canon; that is, two measures after it has begun in one voice, it begins also in another, so that the two become an intertwined whole, each separate yet part of the other. Mahler nicknamed this symphony the "Titan," and, indeed, it is probably the most grandiose first symphony ever written, nearly an hour in length and scored for a very large orchestra. It was thought by some to be too "modern" for audiences of its day, and the first performance was put off until 1889, a full year after the composer had finished it.

Slowly, but don't drag

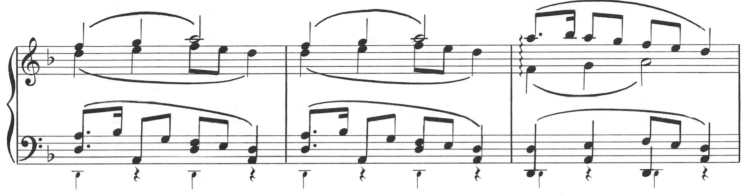

6 Popular Masterpieces in Waltz Time

Tales from the Vienna Woods

Johann Strauss, Jr.

The Vienna Woods enclose the Austrian capital in a 30-mile-wide green belt of unsurpassed magnificence. To this day the Viennese, rich and poor, exalted and humble, walk its green-carpeted paths on warm Sunday afternoons, stopping to sip a glass of wine and listen to the zither music that always seems to fill the air. For Johann Strauss, Jr., years of such Sunday strolls provided the inspiration for this evocative waltz. Written in 1868, it is almost a tone poem as much as a waltz, less for dancing than simply to be enjoyed — like a stroll through the woodland it immortalizes.

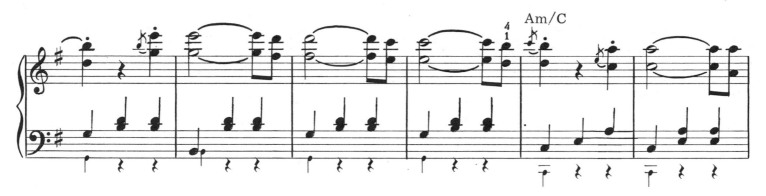

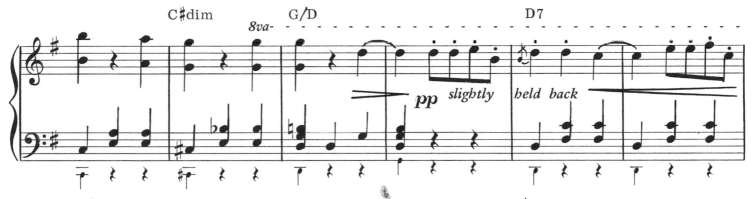

145

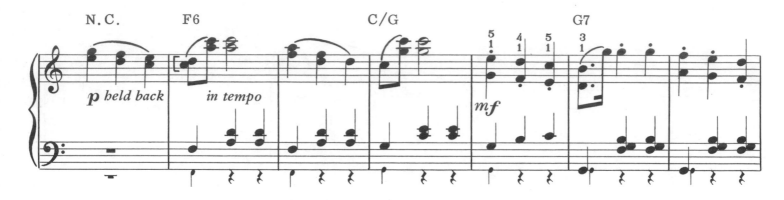

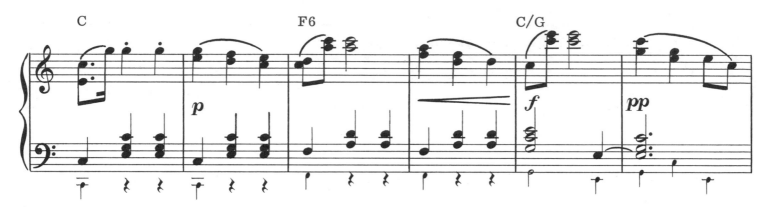

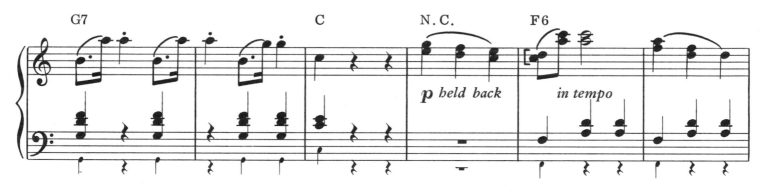

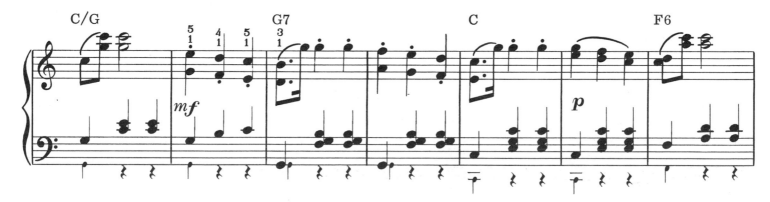

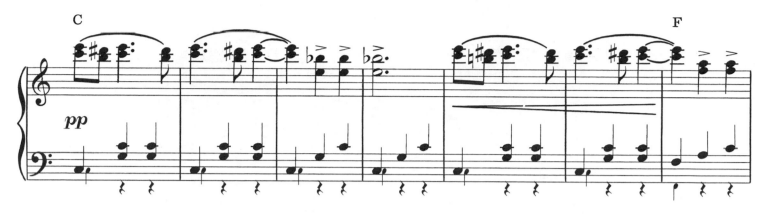

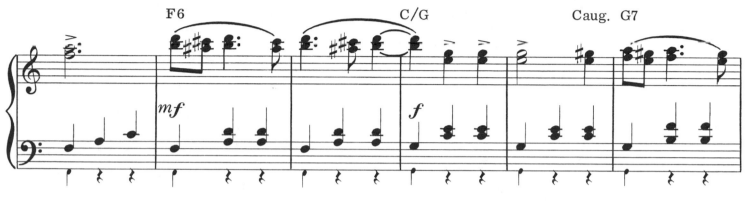

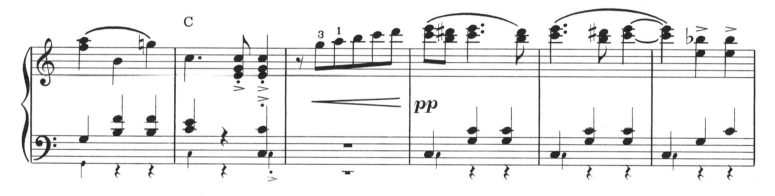

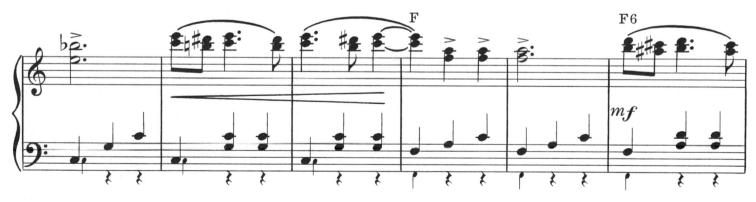

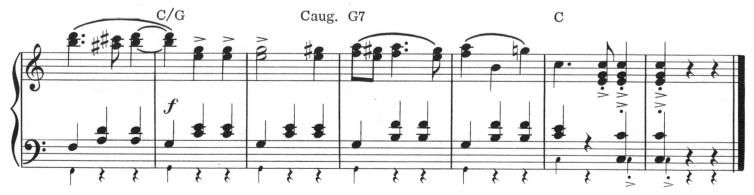

Waves of the Danube

Ion Ivanovici

Moderate, graceful waltz

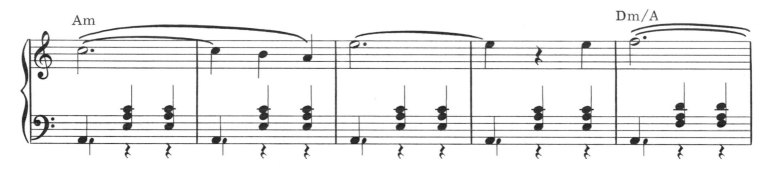

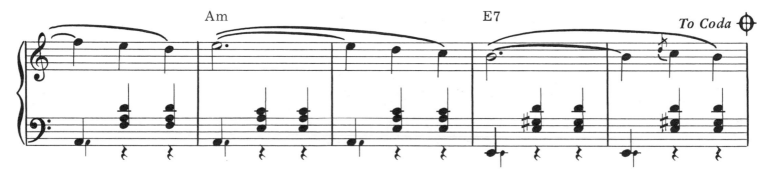

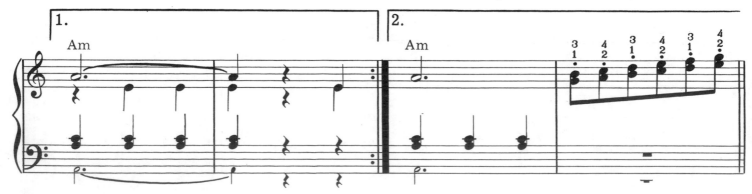

The musical heritage of Rumania is one of the richest — and, alas, least widely known — in all Europe. As would be expected of a country with a Romance language and heritage, Rumanian music tends to be melodically strong. Such pieces as the fiery "Hora Staccato" by Grigoras Dinicu have long been favorites on this side of the Atlantic, and Georges Enesco's "Rumanian Rhapsody," incorporating many popular folk melodies, is frequently heard in concert halls. Perhaps the most popular of all Rumanian imports, however, is "Valurile Dunări," or "Danube Waves," an evocative melody written in 1880 by the bandmaster Ion

Ivanovici. Until the mid-1940s, the piece was known chiefly through its use at Rumanian and Jewish weddings. (Many popular Eastern European melodies have found their way into the folklore of the Jews who lived in those countries.) Then, in 1946, "Danube Waves" turned up in The Jolson Story, a Hollywood screen biography of Al Jolson, the popular entertainer of the 1920s, which starred Larry Parks in the role of Jolson. Songwriting veteran Saul Chaplin adapted Ivanovici's melody to Jolson's own lyrics, and the result was "Anniversary Song," now played at anniversary celebrations all over the world.

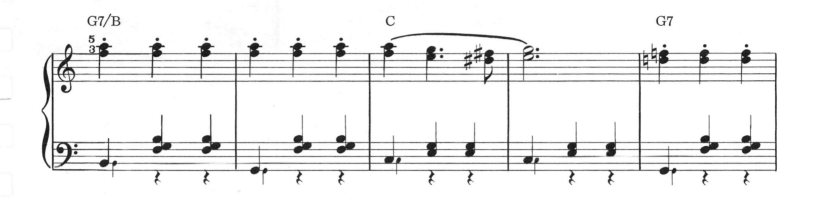

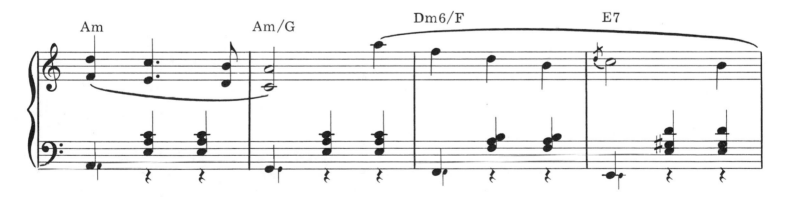

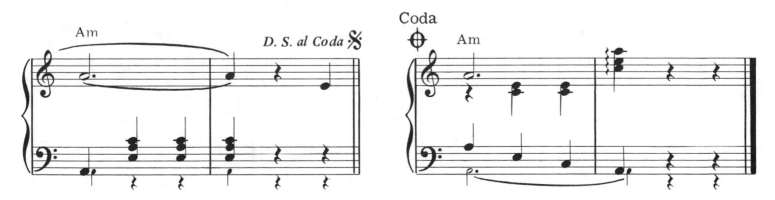

Waltz in B

Johannes Brahms

It would seem unlikely that Vienna's worldly, impulsive, emotionally extravagant Waltz King, Johann Strauss, Jr., should have as an ardent admirer a fussy, unkempt, brusque bachelor from North Germany. But music works strange magic, and those who knew him realized that behind the abrupt manners and baggy clothing he wore, part of Johannes Brahms remained ever young. When Brahms had traveled from his home city of Hamburg to Eternal Vienna in 1862, the music of Strauss permeated the very air itself. The two men became friends — and Brahms' own waltzes reflect that friendship. Brahms autographed one of Frau Strauss's fans by jotting down a few bars of her husband's "Blue Danube" waltz and writing beneath it, "Leider, nicht von — Johannes Brahms" ("Unfortunately, not by — Johannes Brahms"). Certainly the "Waltz in B" (here, for the sake of simplicity, transposed to C) has a lightness and gaiety more redolent of Strauss than of the Brahms we know from his powerful symphonies and towering German Requiem.

Johannes Brahms

Moderately, with spirit

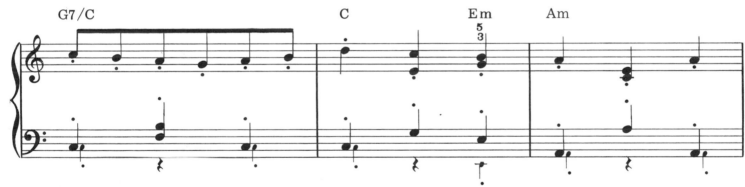

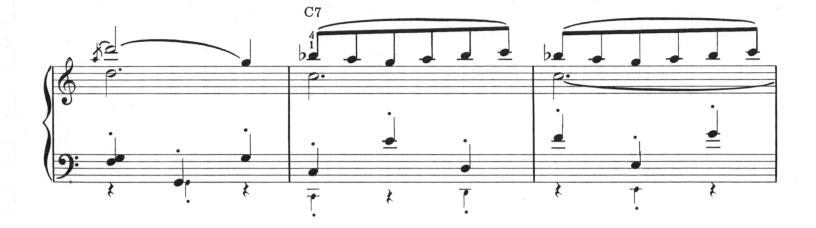

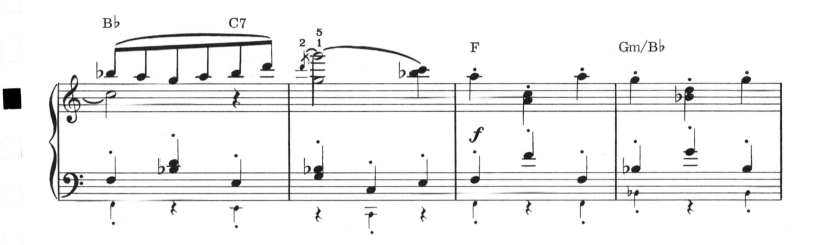

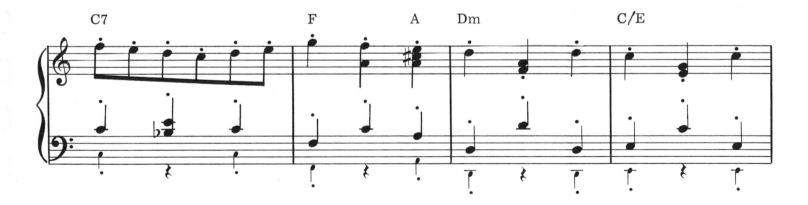

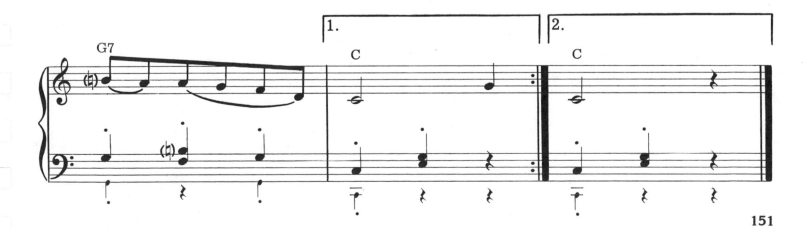

Artist's Life

Johann Strauss, Jr.

Think back to the heady, magical days before the turn of the century. Was an artist's life really like the one described in Giacomo Puccini's La Bohème, when there was little money but plenty of bonhomie, of drink and merriment, of unre-strained dedication to art and love? One might think so on the basis of this beloved waltz by Johann Strauss, Jr. He had established himself as Vienna's Waltz King, carrying on a legacy begun by his father. His orchestra was the talk of Europe, traveling each summer to St. Petersburg (now Leningrad) to entertain the cream of Russian society. More and more, the waltzes that flowed so easily from his pen became idealizations: "Tales from the Vienna Woods" recalling the joys of a Sunday afternoon stroll through the sumptuous Wienerwald that rings the city; "The Blue Danube," a romantic paean to a river that has seldom appeared anything but muddy. And, too, his "Artist's Life." The artist in this musical portrait knows nothing of unpaid bills, watery soup and stale bread; he doesn't shiver through cold winter nights in an unheated garret. There's no room here for despair or soul-searching. This artist's life is all gaiety and good times — and music that cheers the soul.

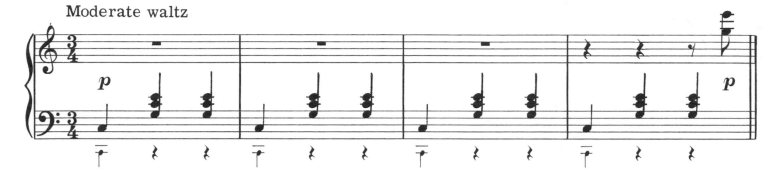

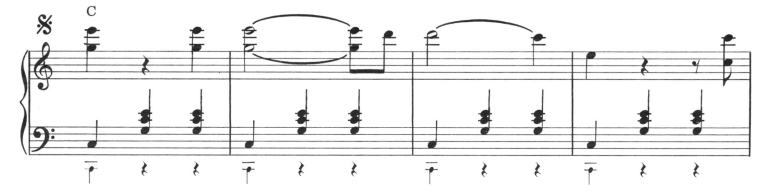

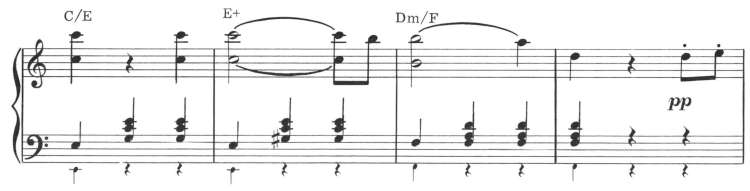

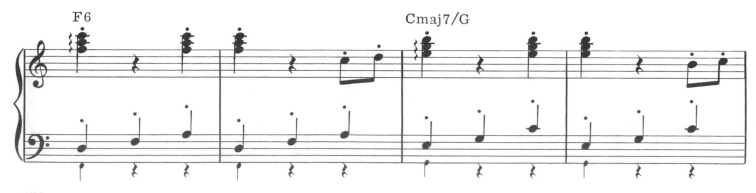

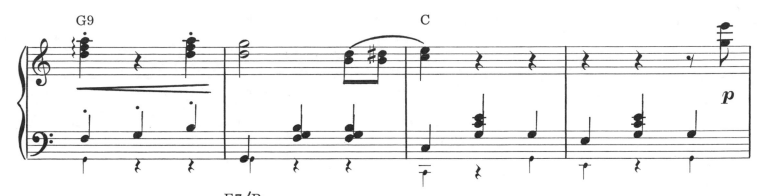

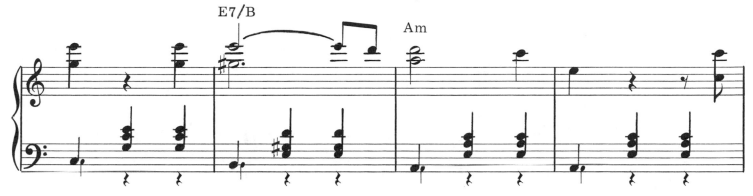

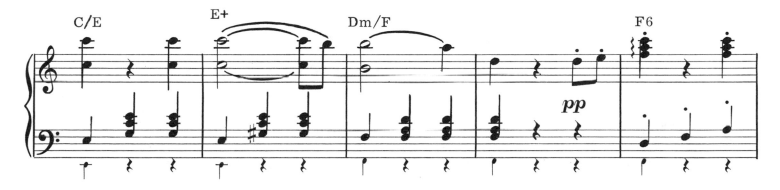

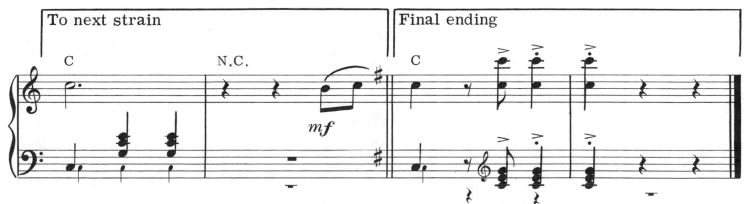

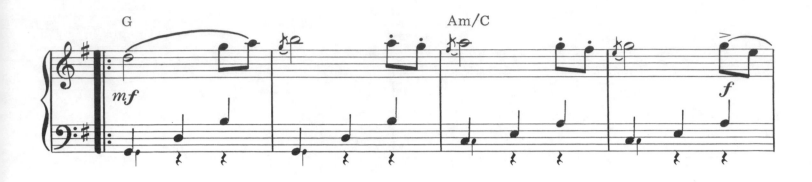

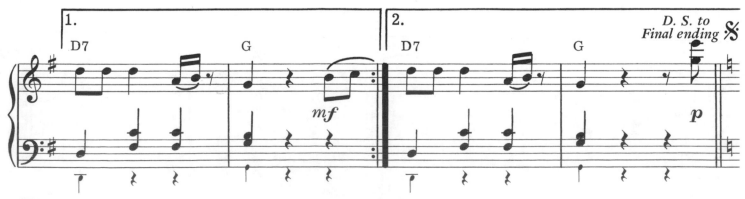

154

La Belle Hélène Waltz

Jacques Offenbach

By the time Jacques Offenbach's Tales of Hoffmann, *which drew on the stories of the multitalented E.T.A. Hoffmann, premiered after the composer's death in 1880, Offenbach had already created a place in history for himself with a series of comic operettas based on subjects drawn from classical mythology. Why mythology? Music scholars agree that the foibles of gods and goddesses were handy metaphors for delivering satiric thrusts at the society of the Second Republic in France*

(the very society, as one writer observed, that lionized Offenbach). But others suggest that something more down-to-earth was involved: Grecian and Roman costumes, being scanty, afforded the female members of Offenbach's casts a chance to show off their figures. La Belle Hélène (1864) depicts the amorous escapades of Helen of Troy. Like the earlier Orpheus in the Underworld, La Belle Hélène *was sharply satiric — a fact presumably lost on the audiences that flocked to see it.*

Moderate waltz tempo

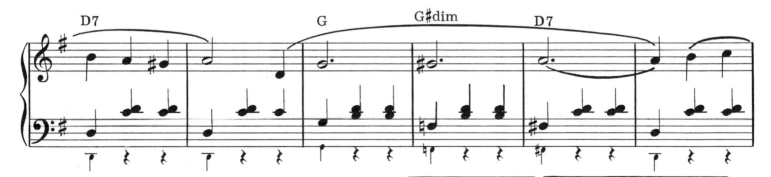

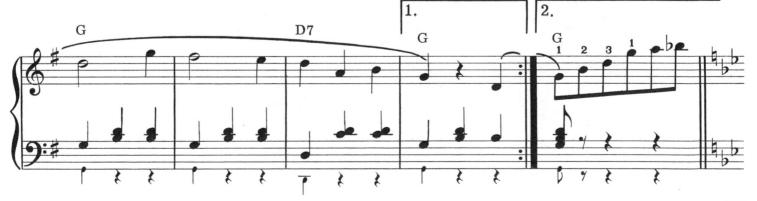

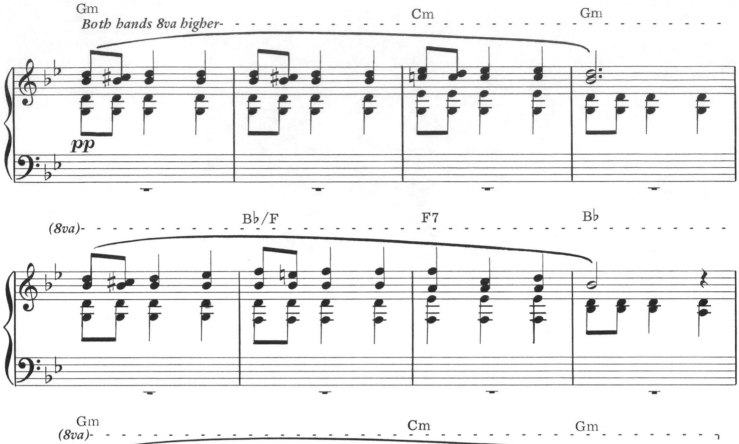

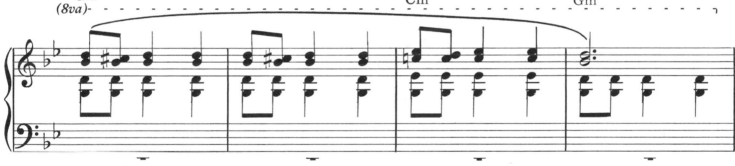

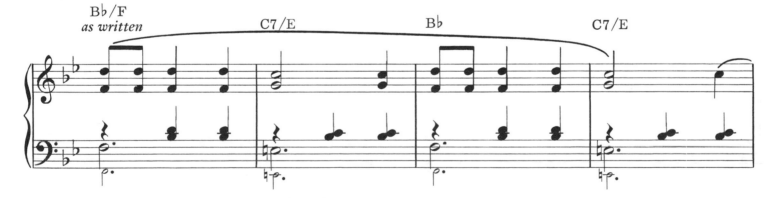

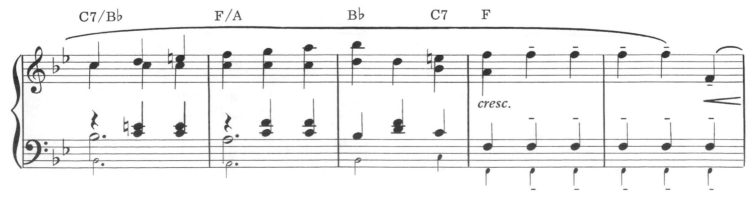

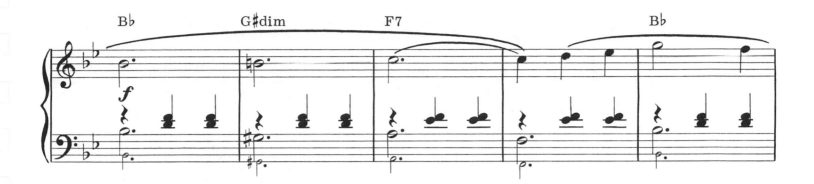

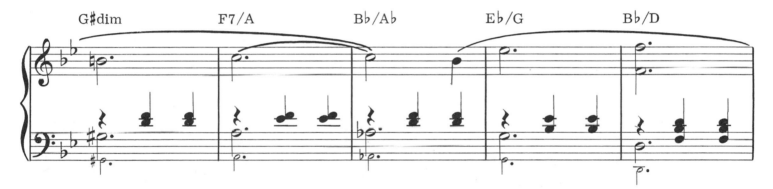

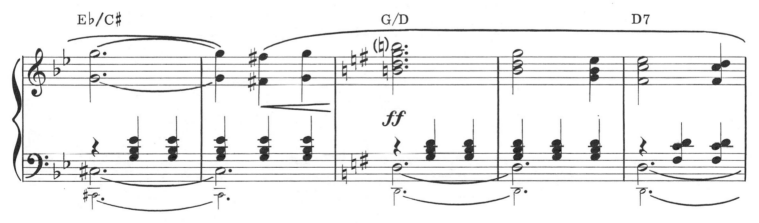

Coppélia Waltz

Léo Delibes

Coppélia (The Girl with the Enamel Eyes) *is a comic ballet masterpiece that turned Léo Delibes from a good journeyman organist and writer of frothy operettas into a composer of substance. And Delibes certainly owes thanks for this transformation to that man of many faces, the unclassifiable E.T.A. Hoffmann. Hoffmann was a writer, essayist, government official, critic, poet and composer. His stories have an air of the fantastic about them — exactly the quality that led Delibes to turn to one of them,* The Sandman, *for inspiration for his new ballet. The plot centers around the efforts of the strange, perhaps slightly mad, Dr. Coppélius, to build ever more lifelike dolls and of the effects of his labors on a romance between two young villagers. Coppélia was performed for the first time at the Paris Opera in May 1870 and since then has been an indispensable feature of the classic ballet repertoire. With its success, Delibes moved on to even greater triumphs with the comic ballet* Sylvia, *then into grand opera with his masterpiece* Lakmé.

Slowly and gracefully

158

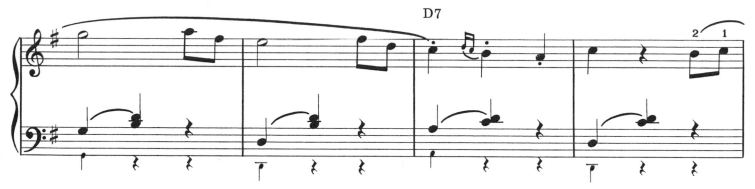

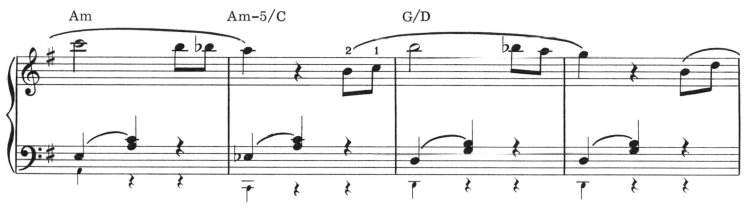

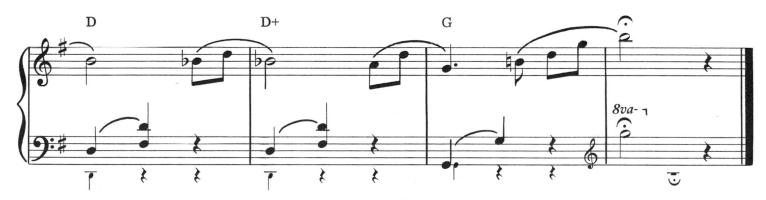

Der Rosenkavalier Waltz

Richard Strauss

Richard Strauss's 1911 opera Der Rosenkavalier (The Knight of the Rose) purports to be a kind of love letter to 18th-century Vienna under the Empress Maria Theresa. In truth, however, the flavor and atmosphere are far more reminiscent of the same city a century later, and the gracefully sweeping waltzes forming its musical axis are strongly redolent of that other notable Strauss — Waltz King Johann Strauss, Jr. (who was, however, no relation). The plot is a dizzy round of mistaken identities, disguises, plotting lovers and petty intrigues, all ending happily. Three-quarters of a century after its premiere, Der Rosenkavalier remains the most beloved of the composer's works.

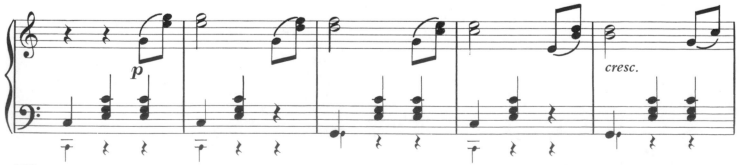

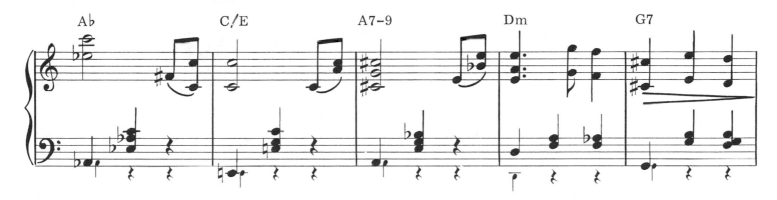

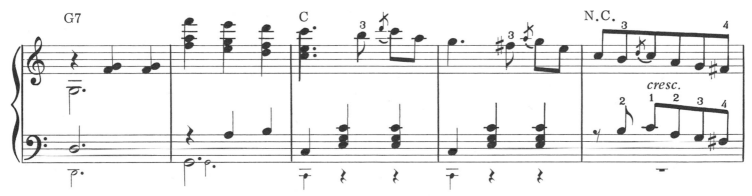

Although more often than not Tchaikovsky's moods sank to the depths of depression, much of the melancholy Russian composer's music is bright and full of melodies of extraordinary beauty. One example is the music for his ballet The Sleeping Beauty. Everything about it was — and is — magnificent. And yet, surprisingly, reactions to the premiere of the work, on January 15, 1890, were mixed, and Tchaikovsky went into his usual fit of self-recrimination. But his disappointment was brief: The Sleeping Beauty went on to enjoy immense popularity, with this most gracious of waltzes perhaps most beloved of all.

Peter Ilych Tchaikovsky

The Sleeping Beauty Waltz

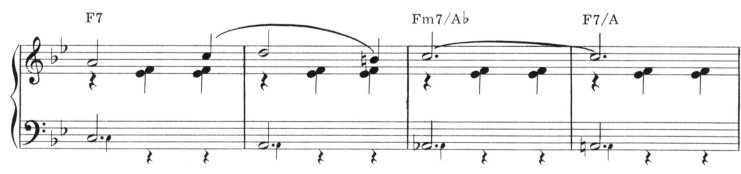

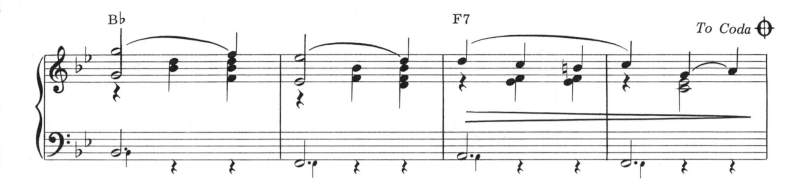

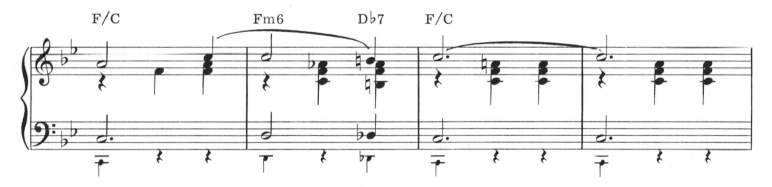

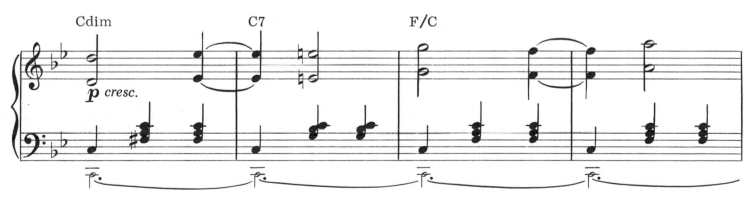

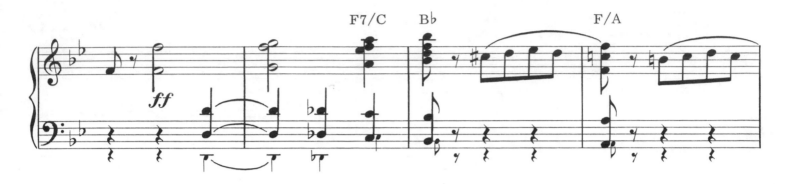

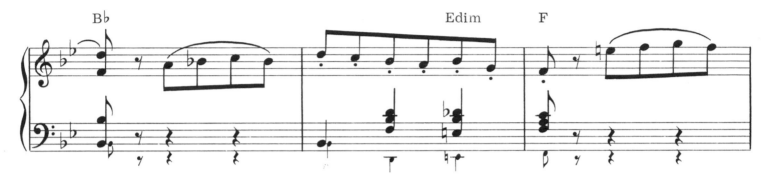

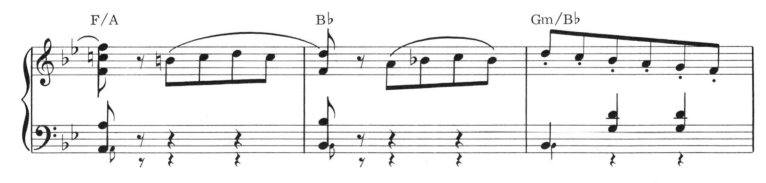

D.S. al Coda 𝄌

Coda

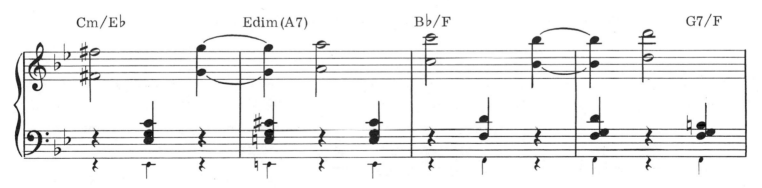

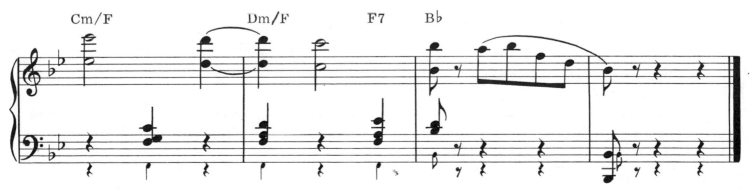

Peter Ilych Tchaikovsky

Andante Cantabile

In 1871, Tchaikovsky, who was visiting his sister Alexandra near Kiev, jotted down an engaging little tune that he heard being sung by a house painter. The tune became the basis for the slow movement of the composer's String Quartet in D — "Andante Cantabile," meaning relaxed and in a singing fashion. In the late 1930s and early '40s, when popular songwriters were tapping Tchaikovsky's music for inspiration, this gorgeous melody was adapted as "On the Isle of May."

Peter Ilych Tchaikovsky

Andante cantabile (not fast, but in a smooth singing manner)

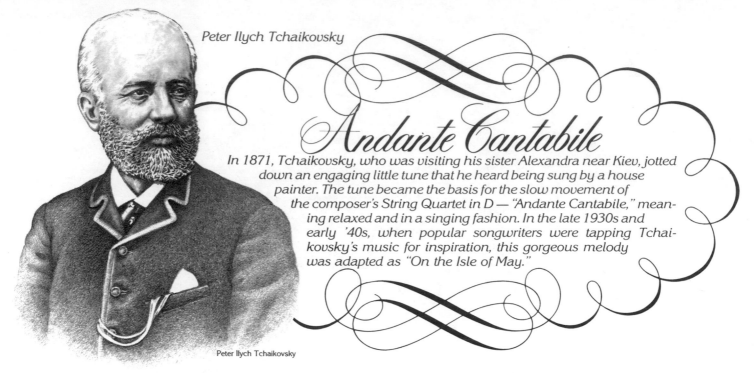

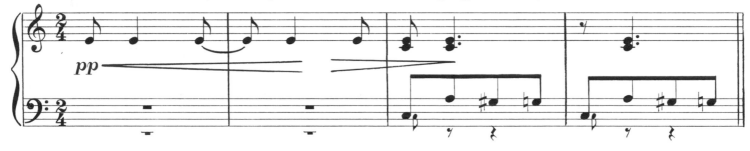

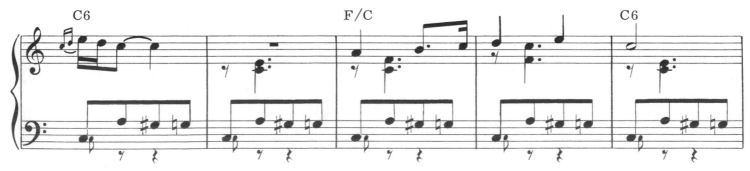

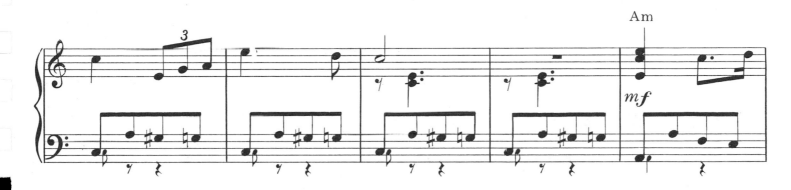

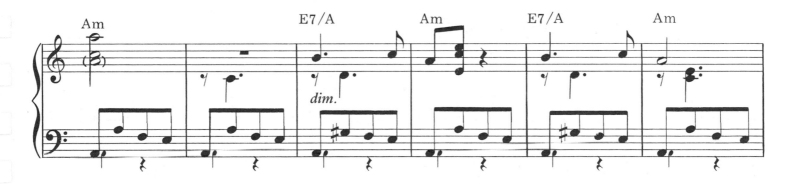

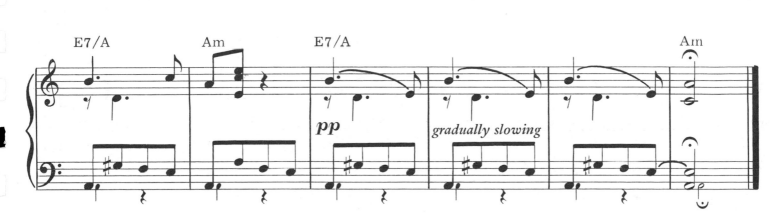

The Nutcracker Mini-Suite

Peter Ilych Tchaikovsky

When he began composing The Nutcracker, Tchaikovsky was more than a little apprehensive. Neither of his earlier ballets, Swan Lake and The Sleeping Beauty, had been greeted with immediate acclaim by critics and audiences. Yet the theme of The Nutcracker intrigued him. In E.T.A. Hoffmann's imaginative tale, the toys under a Christmas tree come alive. They are terrorized by a dictatorial Mouse King until a soldier-shaped nutcracker assumes the role of Prince Charming and drives the villain off. Although Tchaikovsky was 51 when he composed The Nutcracker, he still retained a childlike fascination with the fantastic. As things turned out, the composer was afforded a preview of his work's stunning success. Before the ballet had ever been performed, he stitched together six themes from it into an orchestral suite to be played by the Russian Musical Society. The Nutcracker Suite brought down the house — and is still a concert favorite. The two themes here — the "March Miniature" and the pastoral "Dance of the Reed Flutes" (page 170) — are among its most beloved moments.

March Miniature

Bright march tempo

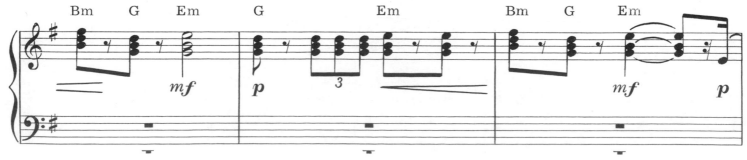

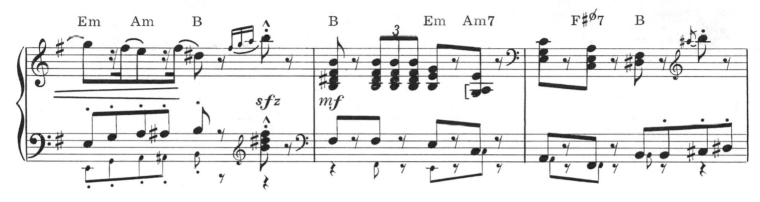

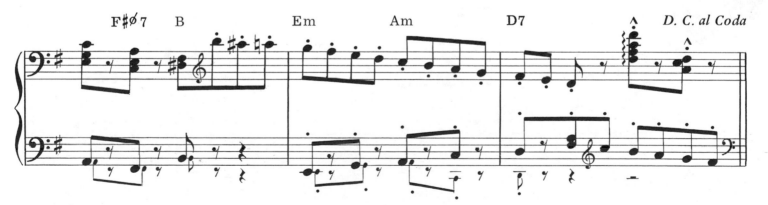

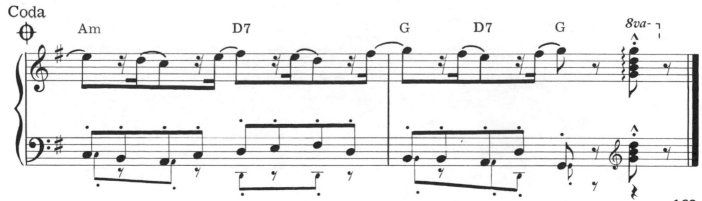

Dance of the Reed Flutes

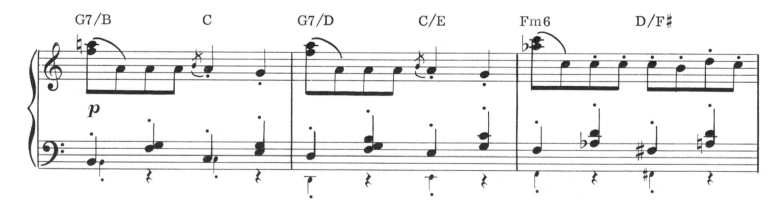

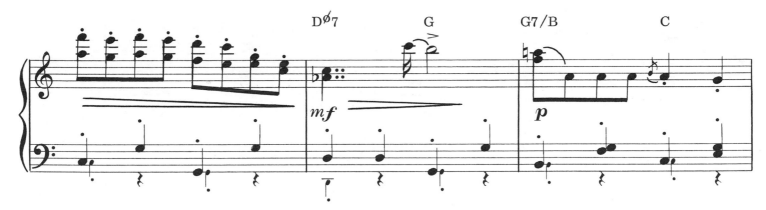

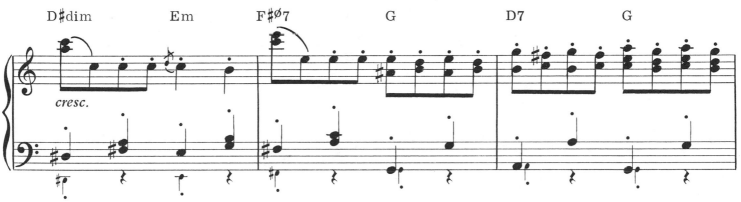

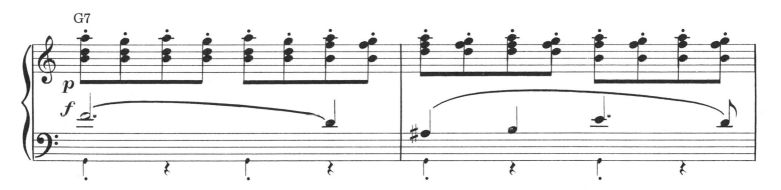

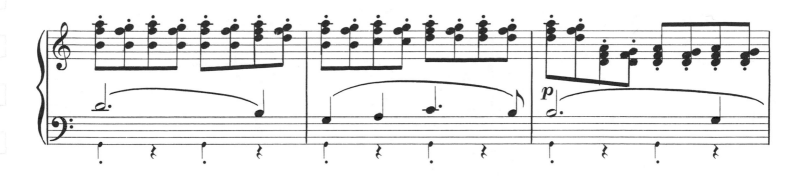

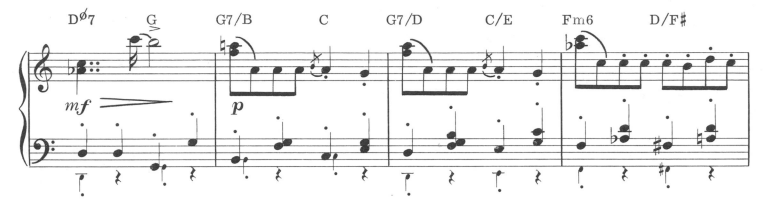

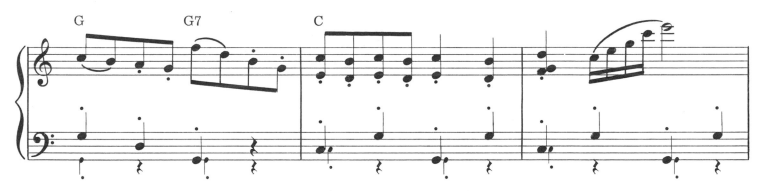

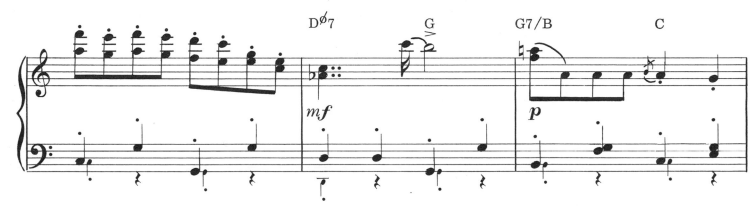

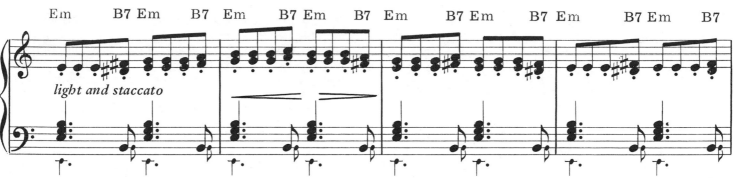

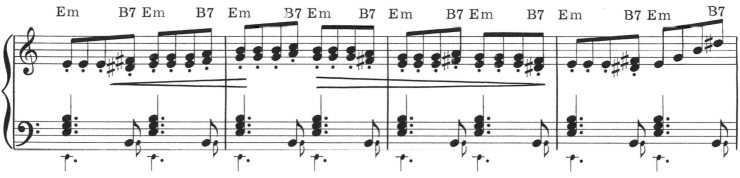

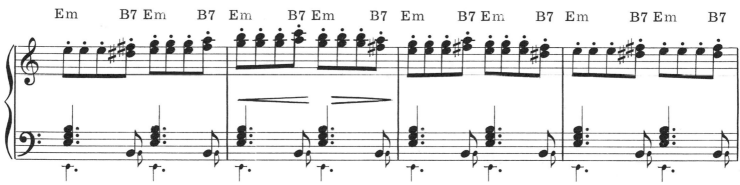

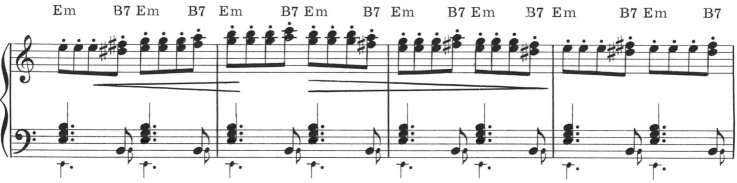

D. S. al Fine

Eugene Onegin Waltz

Peter Ilych Tchaikovsky

The following comes from the pen of Tchaikovsky and dates from around the time that he began composing **Eugene Onegin**, based on a poem by Alexander Pushkin. "How delightful," he wrote, "to avoid the commonplace pharaohs, Ethiopian princesses, poisoned cups and all the rest. The wreath of poetry...joined to Pushkin's inspired verse will compensate for what it lacks in other respects." The reference was clearly to Giuseppi Verdi's opera **Aïda** but could as well have applied to dozens of other overblown, melodramatic librettos. Pushkin's story, by contrast, is small and inward-looking. The young and impressionable Tatiana grows through and beyond her love for Onegin, a spoiled, haughty, self-indulgent young man, into greater awareness and responsibility. Before that happens, at least one good friend dies needlessly and several others confront each other in unexpected ways. It is a surprisingly modern story, and Tchaikovsky's magnificent music helped make it the most famous of the composer's 10 operas and the one most widely performed in Russia. This waltz is played at Tatiana's birthday ball, where she dances with Onegin for the first time and where the story begins to unfold.

Moderately

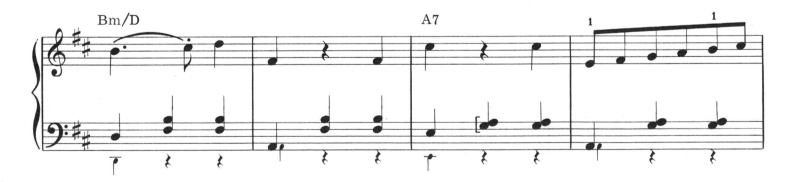

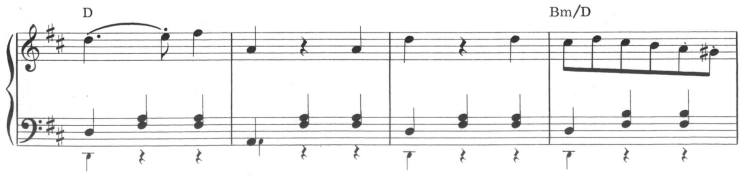

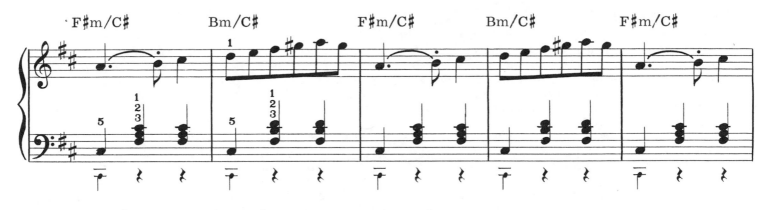

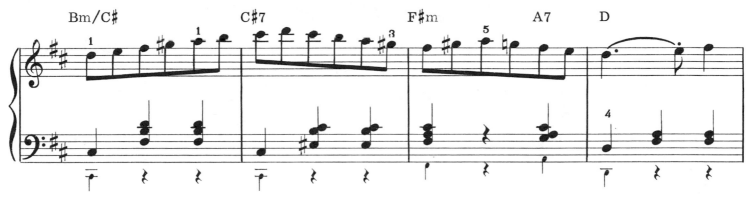

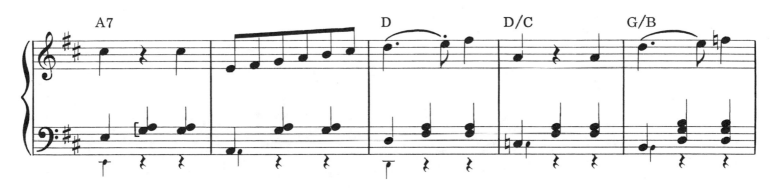

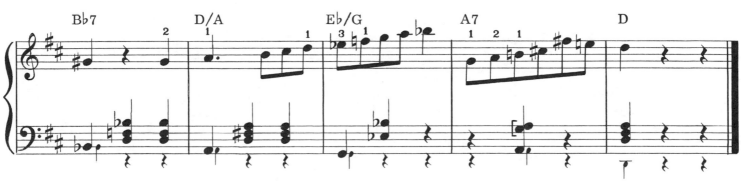

Swan Lake - Overture to Act II

Peter Ilych Tchaikovsky

It's always surprising to learn that Tchaikovsky considered *Swan Lake* — now perhaps the most revered of all ballets — an abject failure. His work on it went smoothly enough. Even an interruption to cover the Bayreuth Festival in Germany for a Moscow newspaper was helpful. Hearing Richard Wagner's music there helped snap the 30-year-old composer out of a long and dark period of depression. Inspired, too, by Delibes' recently completed *Coppélia*, he finished work on *Swan Lake* quickly and with enthusiasm, but from that point on things began to go wrong. Both the choreographer and conductor chopped up his score, and an aging, temperamental ballerina insisted on substituting her specialties from other ballets in place of his carefully wrought solo pieces. The corps de ballet stumbled around, according to one account, "like sleepy children in want of naps." The sets were clumsy, the costumes a joke. Characteristically, Tchaikovsky blamed himself and tumbled back into the abyss of depression. Yet in 1895, little more than a year after his death, *Swan Lake* was revived, staged properly — and history, gloriously, knows the rest.

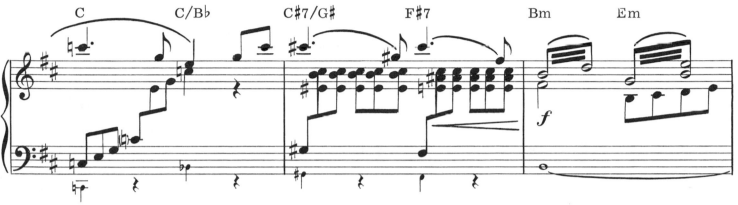

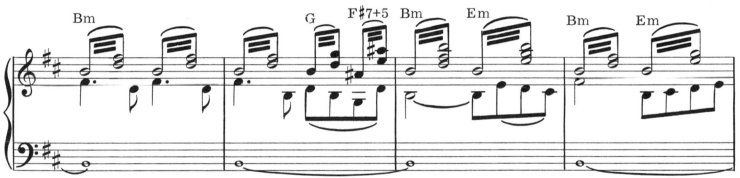

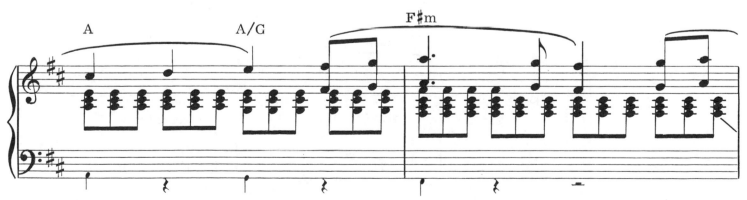

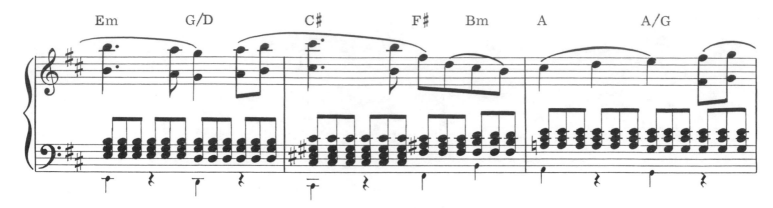

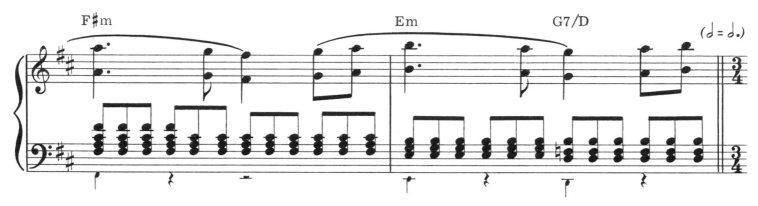

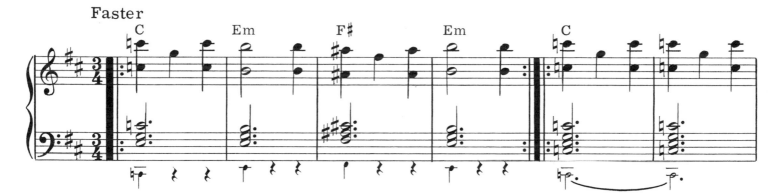

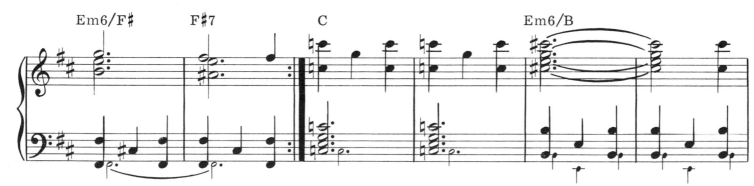

Faster than the original tempo

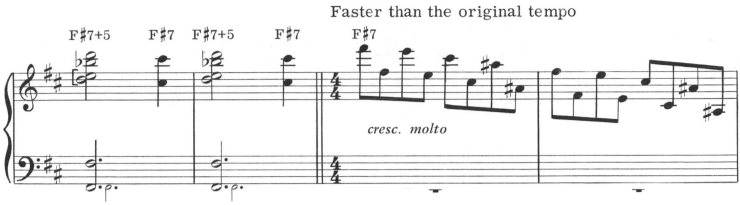

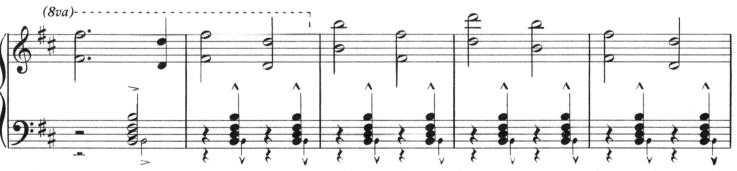

Song Without Words

Peter Ilych Tchaikovsky

Swan Lake and all Tchaikovsky's other triumphs lay far in the future in 1867, when he
wrote the charming "Song Without Words" ("Chant sans paroles"), third of three pieces for piano in a light
salon style popular in the mid-19th century. He was young, full of ambition and energy, and determined to put an enervating
apprenticeship in law behind him and seek his destiny as a composer. On a vacation in Finland, he and his
younger brother Anatole soon ran out of money (Tchaikovsky was always improvident)
but managed to reach the Baltic coastal resort town of Hapsal in Estonia, where Vera Vasilevna Davidova, a
gifted amateur pianist who was related to their sister by marriage, lived. She welcomed them
extravagantly, played hostess to them and made sure they had funds to get home.
In gratitude, Tchaikovsky dedicated the three piano pieces —
published as Souvenir of Hapsal — to her.

Allegretto grazioso e cantabile
(Not fast, but gracefully with a songlike tone)

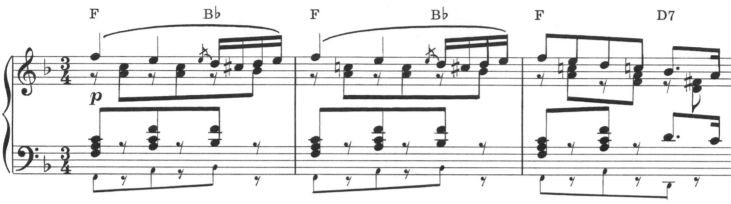

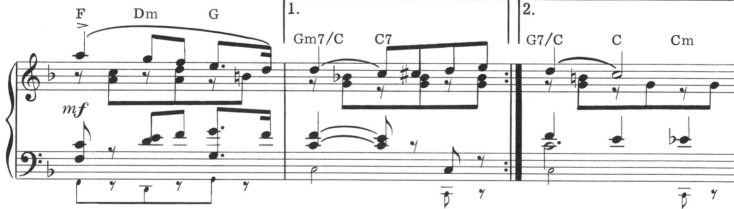

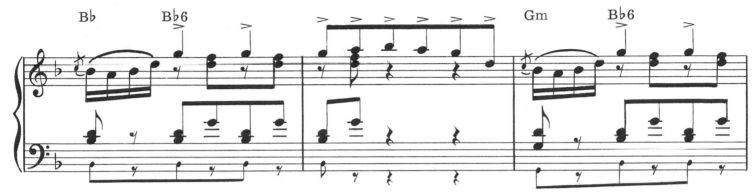

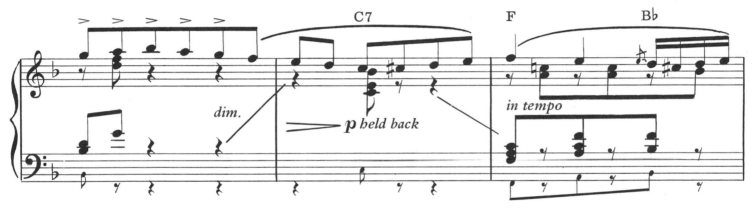

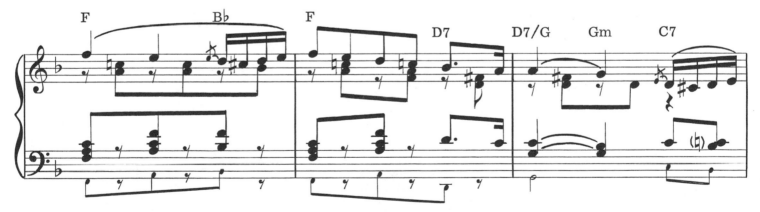

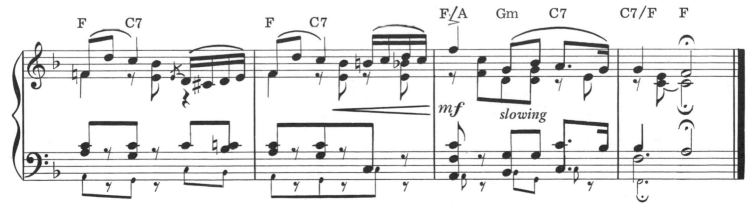

Waltz from Symphony No. 5

Peter Ilych Tchaikovsky

It's hard to imagine, listening to the succession of beautiful melodies throughout Tchaikovsky's Fifth Symphony, how critics could have found it wanting in imagination. At least one writer wondered in print whether the composer's melodic gift was "exhausted and played out." Now it is generally accepted that if any one symphony represents the peak of Tchaikovsky's art, it is this. Themes from the second movement have given us two lovely popular songs ("Moon Love" and "Long May We Love"). This waltz is something of an anomaly, placed by the composer where a scherzo is normally used. Controlled, elegant — somehow shadowed by restraint — it never quite lets go, even in the gay spiccato for strings.

Moderate waltz tempo

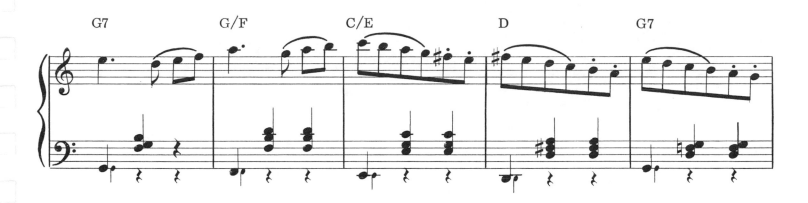

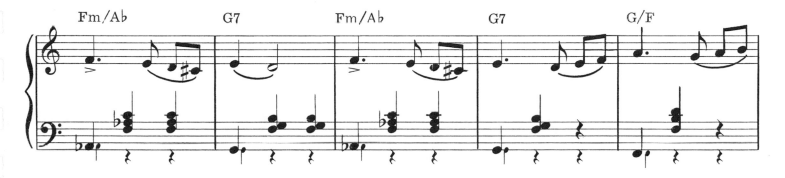

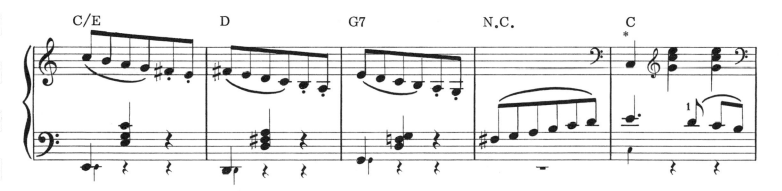

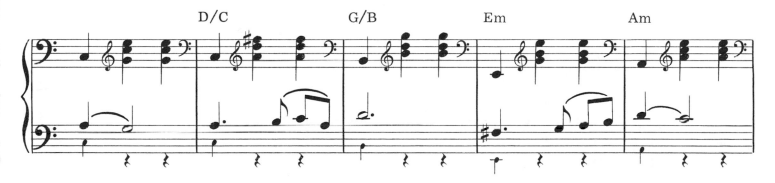

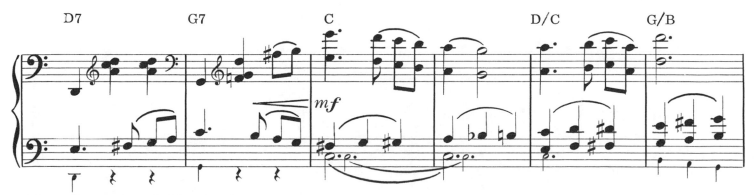

Organ players may omit this and analogous bass notes.

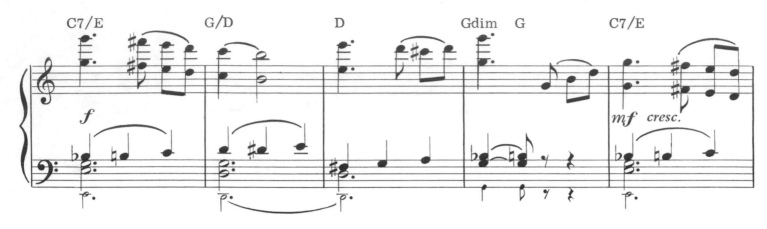

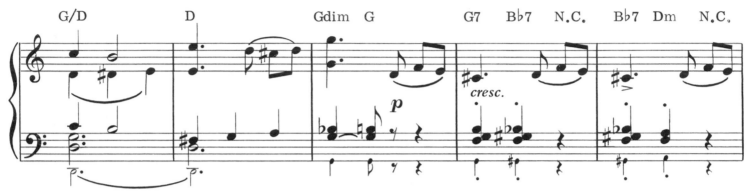

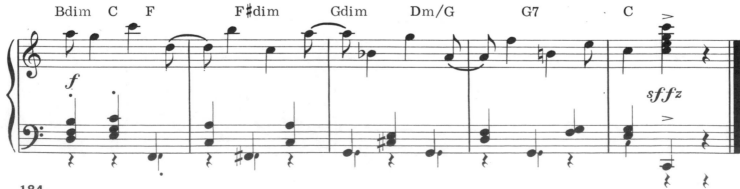

Marche Slav

Peter Ilych Tchaikovsky

Not unexpectedly, there's a story behind this most patriotic of Russian works. At the time it was written in 1876, the principality of Serbia was in rebellion against Turkey, which had dominated many of the Slavic peoples on and off since the 14th century. The Turks had a well-merited reputation for cruelty, and the struggle for Serbian independence was long and bitter. Under the terms of the treaty ending the 1828-29 Russo-Turkish War, Serbia was placed under the protection of Russia, and therefore Russia had declared itself for Serbia in the cause of Slav solidarity. Against this tumultuous political back-ground, Tchaikovsky composed this stirring show-piece, climaxing in an all-stops-out rendition of "God Preserve the Tsar." It was played at a concert held in St. Petersburg to raise funds for Serbian troops wounded in the fighting. Like the composer's "1812 Overture," the "Marche Slav" is more fire than content—but it whipped the opening-night audience's emotions to near-hysteria. To paraphrase one wit, just imagine the effect of a medley of "God Bless America," "The Stars and Stripes Forever," "White Christmas" and "Dixie," played fortissimo, while American troops march off to defend Plymouth Rock.

Moderately, in the style of a funeral march

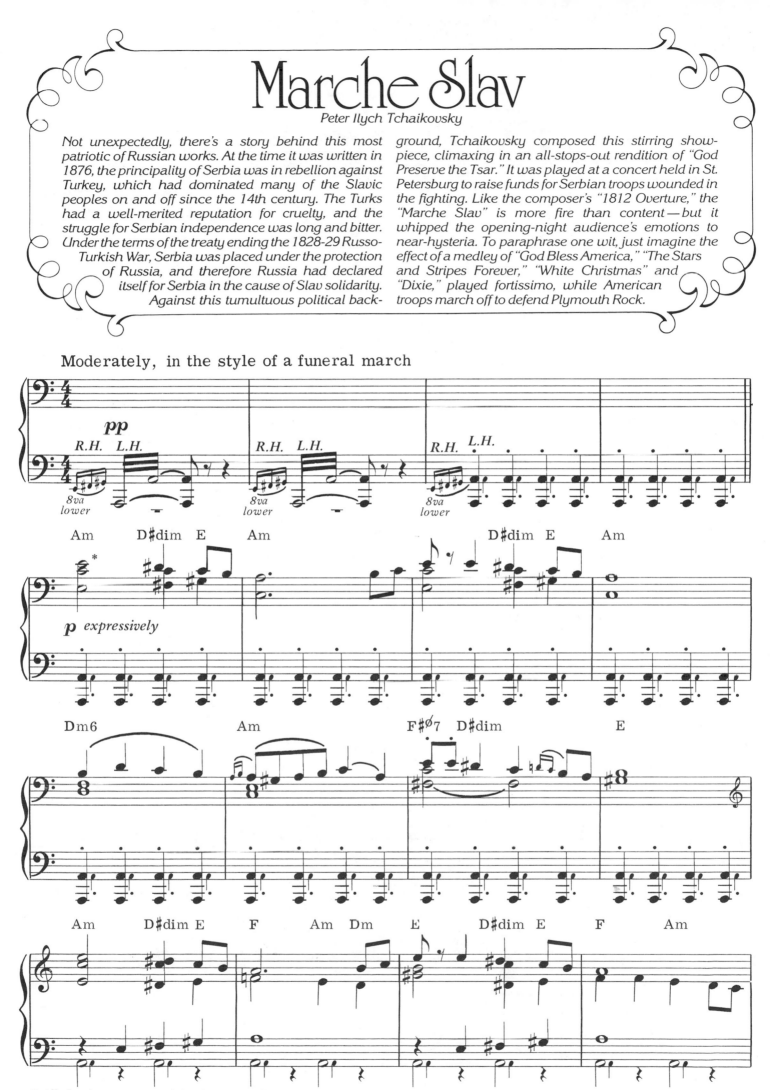

* All chords over an A pedal point except for measures 21-29.

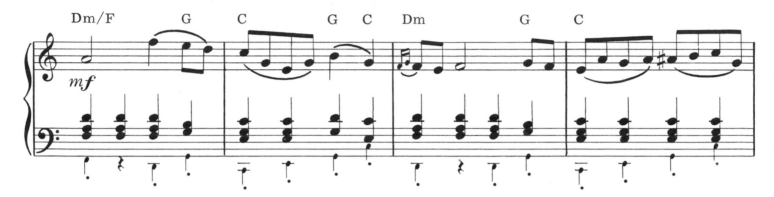

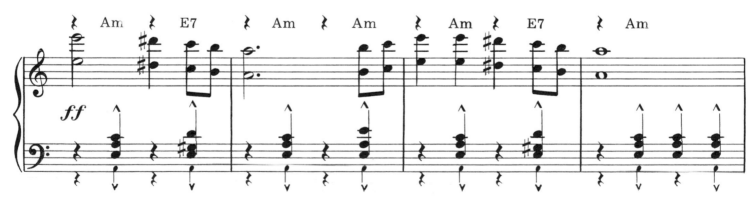

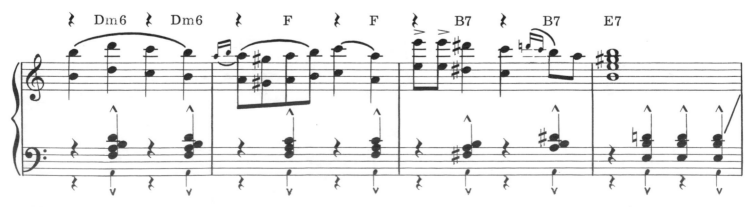

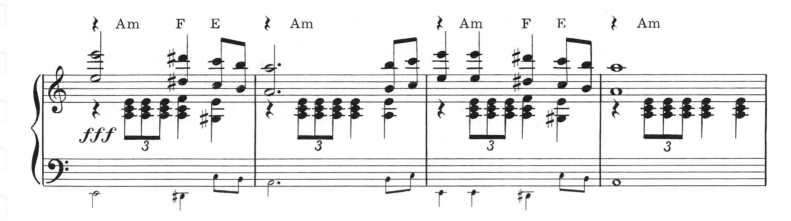

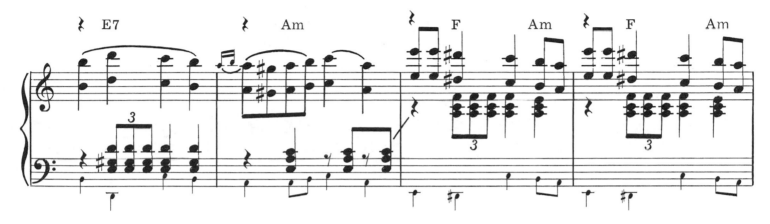

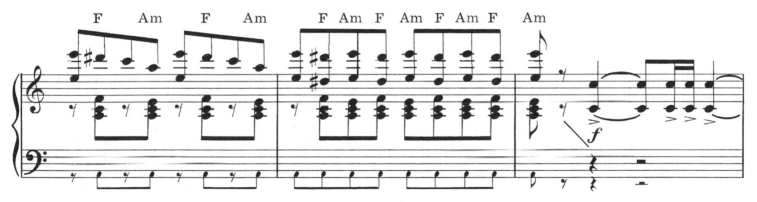

8 Melodic Highlights from Instrumental Masterworks

Franz Schubert's music for the play Rosamunde, written in 1823, was little known for many years after the composer's death. It was discovered and restored to prominence by musicologist George Grove and Sir Arthur Sullivan (of Gilbert and Sullivan). Schubert borrowed the theme for the Overture from music that he had written for a melodrama called The Magic Harp, which had failed three years previously. The much-played Entr'acte (page 190) contains some of the most beautiful melody ever written. The Ballet excerpt (page 191), which Dan Fox has incorporated in his suite, is a close relative of Schubert's famed "Marche Militaire."

Franz Schubert

Arranged by Dan Fox

Rosamunde Suite
Theme from Overture

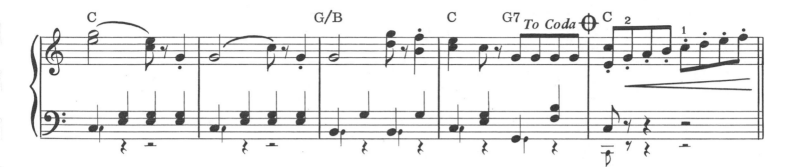

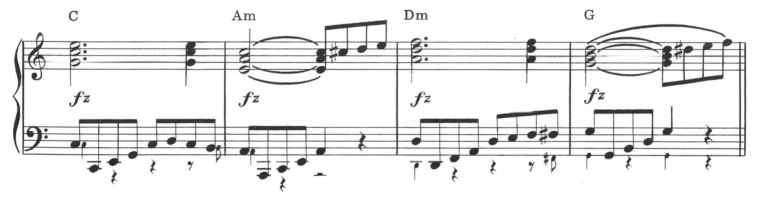

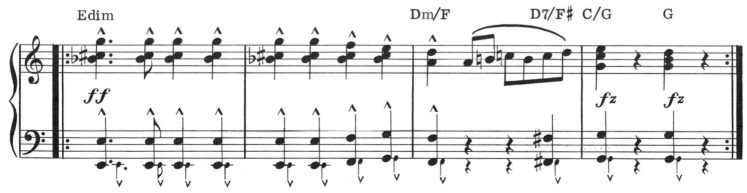

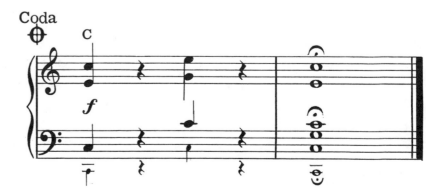

Entr'acte No.3

Andante con moto (not fast and with a flowing forward motion)

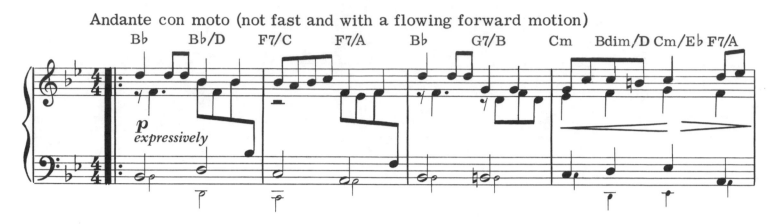

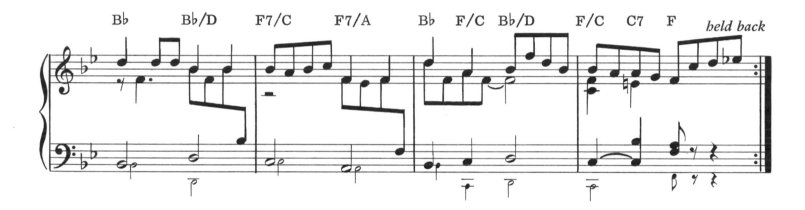

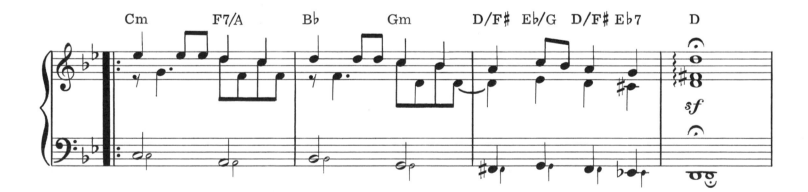

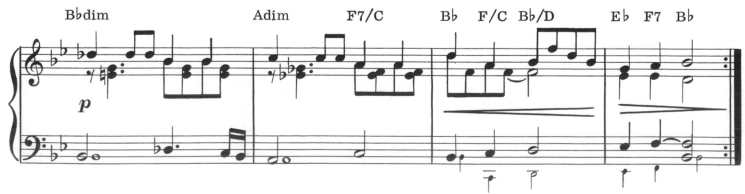

Ballet Music No. 2

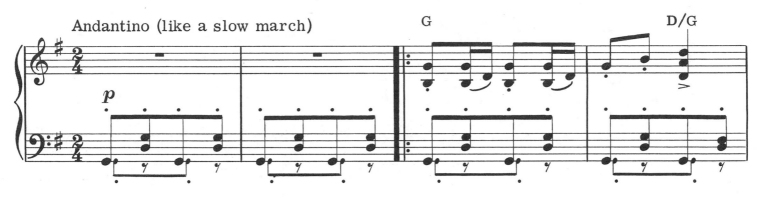

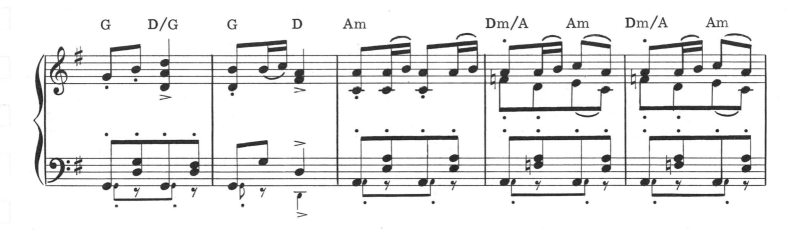

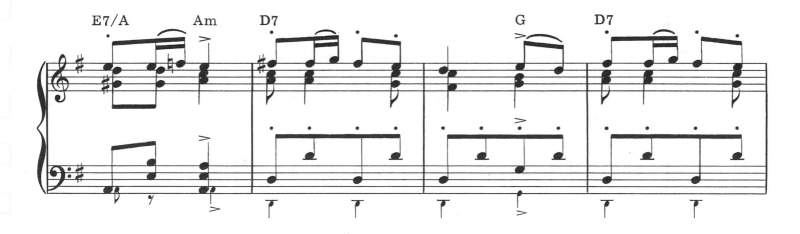

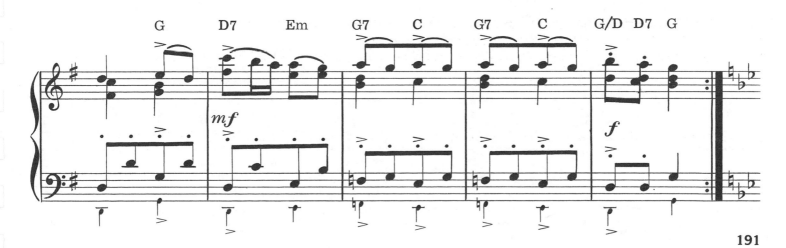

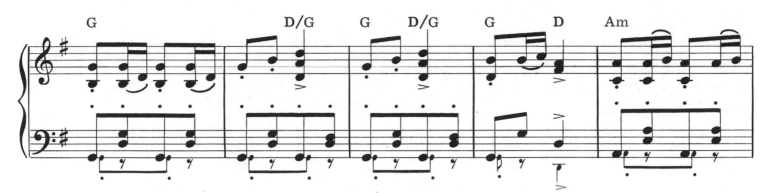

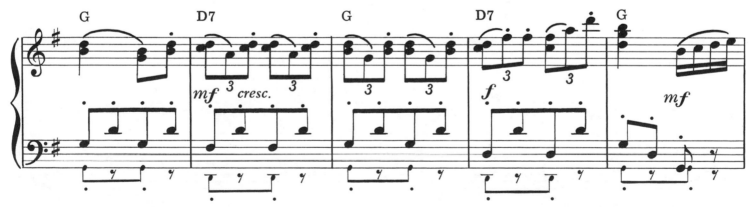

"Trout" Quintet Theme

Franz Schubert

Throughout his brief life, Schubert often lacked money, but he never wanted for admirers, those well-to-do Viennese who attended the regular "Schubertiads," or evenings devoted to performances of his works, at various homes around the city. One such admirer was the baritone Johann Michael Vogl, and during the summer of 1819, Schubert accompanied his colleague and fan on a vacation trip to Vogl's hometown of Steyr, in the Austrian Alps. The sojourn in Steyr turned out to be one of the happiest periods of Schubert's life. Sylvester Paumgartner, one of their hosts during this holiday, was an amateur cellist and suggested that the composer write a piece for a small piano-and-strings ensemble made up of local players. Pressing his advantage as host, he further requested that there be some reference in the piece to one of his favorite Schubert songs, "Die Forelle" (The Trout). The result was the "Trout" Quintet, written for violin, viola, cello, bass and piano. According to most accounts, Schubert did not write a score but instead wrote out parts for the participants. The fourth movement is actually a set of variations on the two-part "Trout" theme: the strings set it out first, after which the piano enters with the first variation. The "Trout" Quintet (which is also known as the Quintet in A) was first performed officially that December at Paumgartner's home.

Allegretto (not fast, but in 2; ♩ = 1 beat)

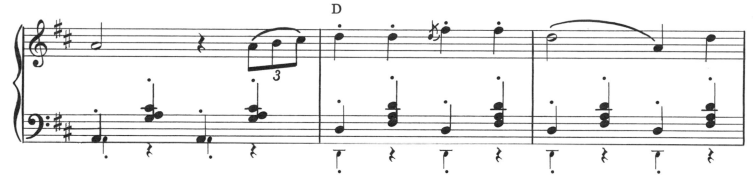

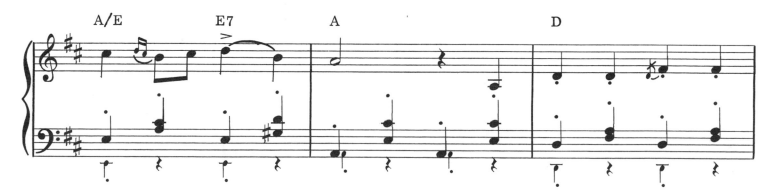

194

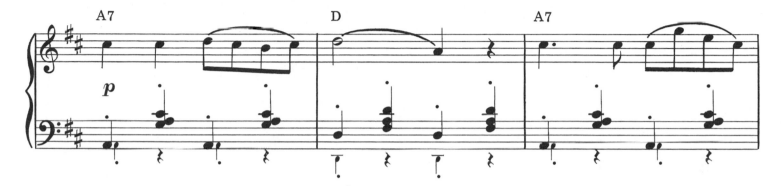

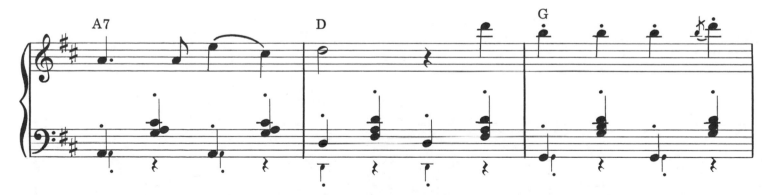

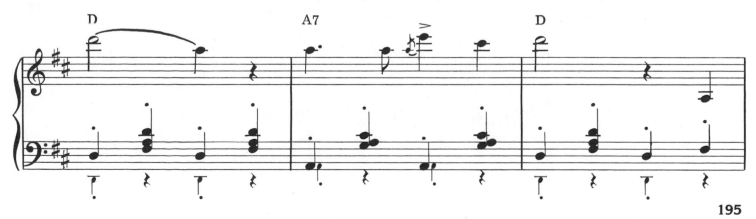

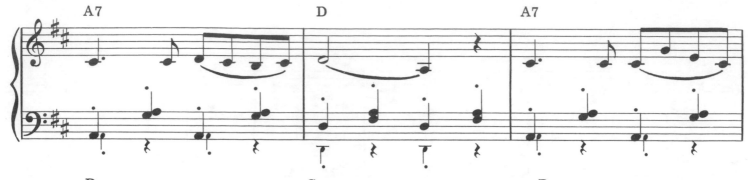

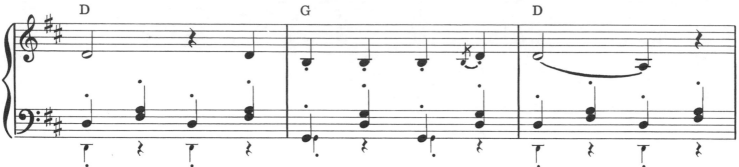

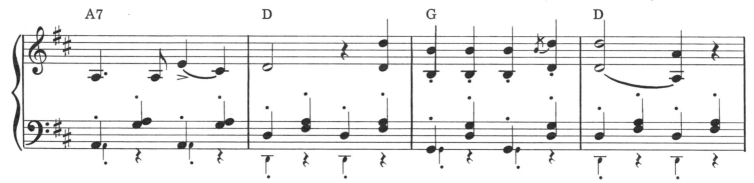

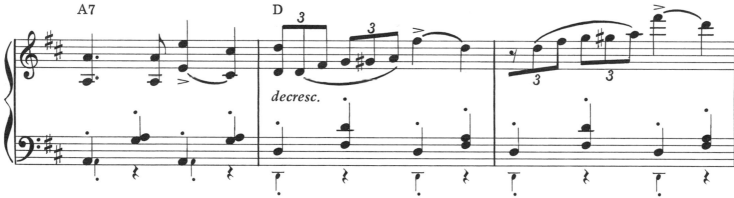

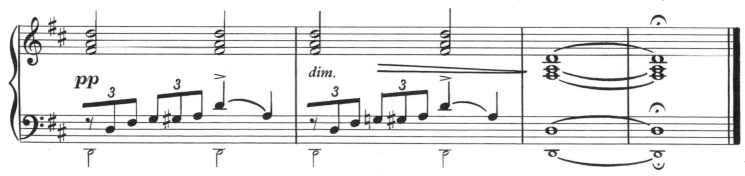

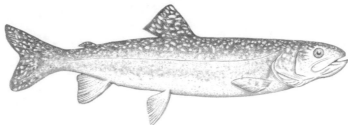

Eine kleine Nachtmusik

Wolfgang Amadeus Mozart

Eine kleine Nachtmusik (A Little Night Music) *is a small confection for strings that Mozart whipped up for an unknown occasion — perhaps a birthday, a wedding or an anniversary. It is the equivalent in 18th-century terms of a song written for a television commercial or for presentation at an industrial show: music to order, for the entertainment of the comfortable burghers of Austria. Yet the quality and the melodic felicity that went into this small serenade are equal in their way to the best of the composer's operas, concertos and symphonies. Mozart wrote many such divertimentos — light social music, not to be taken seriously.* Eine kleine Nachtmusik *dates from 1787, a period when Mozart was hard at work on his opera* Don Giovanni, *yet there is no indication here of anything casual or superficial in the composing. The four movements — sonatina, romanza, minuet and rondo — are small gems, each with melodic grace and sublime inner balance. Excerpted here are the themes from the first two movements.*

Wolfgang Amadeus Mozart

Opening Theme

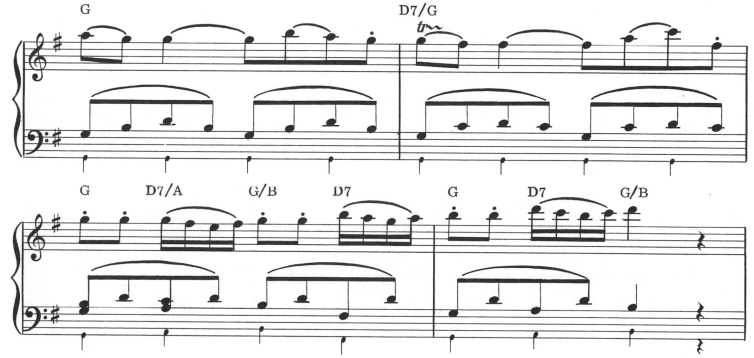

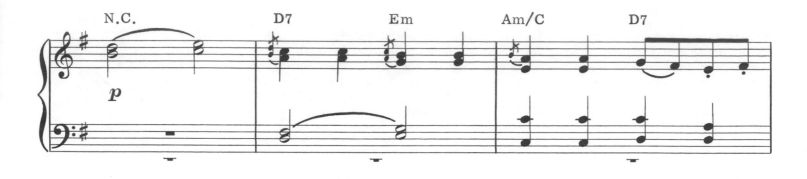

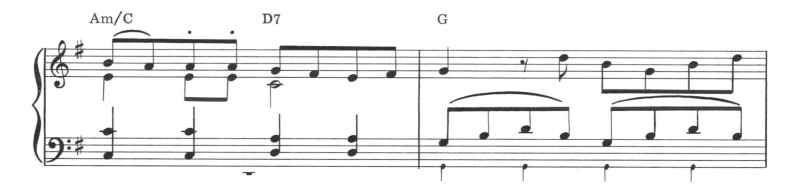

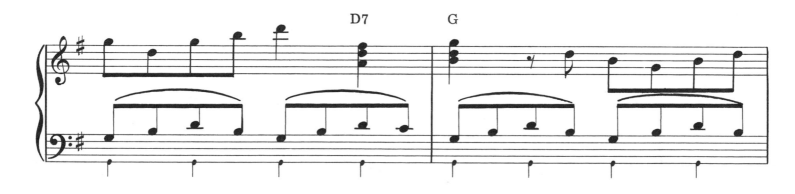

Romanza

Beethoven: Violin Concerto

First Movement–Second Theme

Ludwig van Beethoven

In a major sense, the history of great solo instrumental concertos is a history of the great solo players, and no soloist plays a more distinguished role than the violinist Joseph Joachim. Born in 1831 near Bratislava in what is now Czechoslovakia, he entered the Leipzig Conservatory at age 12 and a year later gave a performance of Beethoven's Violin Concerto, with Felix Mendelssohn conducting, which made instant history. The concerto had been part of the orchestral repertoire since its premiere in 1806 and had been performed by several distinguished violinists. But somehow the stigma of its first performance, which had been grievously marred by the antics of violinist Franz Clement, had remained: the public had largely ignored the work. But so warm, so vibrant was the young Joachim's performance

that an immediate reassessment of the Beethoven masterpiece was unavoidable. (It was Joachim to whom Brahms, some years later, dedicated his only violin concerto.) In the words of musicologist Percy Scholes, "There was a high idealism in all that Joachim did, combined with great technical skill and deep interpretative insight." The violinist was also a skilled composer and conductor, as well as founder of the leading string quartet of the late 19th century. In the concerto that he helped to revive, each of the themes offers something distinctive. (Themes from the second and third movements begin on page 203.) Below is the second theme from the opening movement, with its deceptively easy-sounding line of octaves with which the solo violin enters in the first movement (just try to play them!).

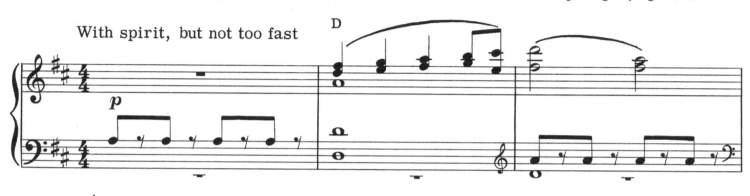

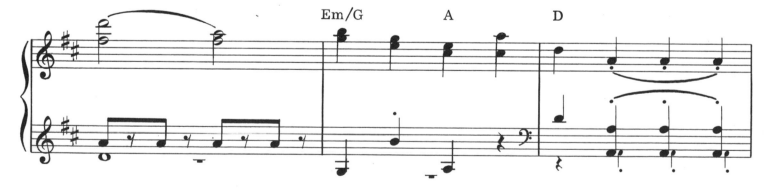

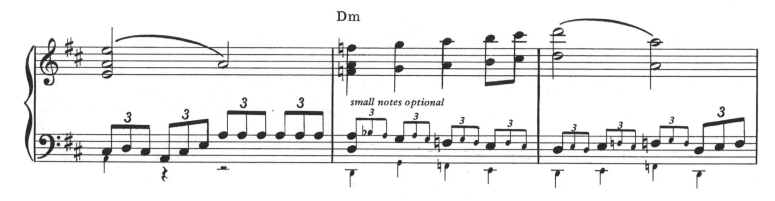

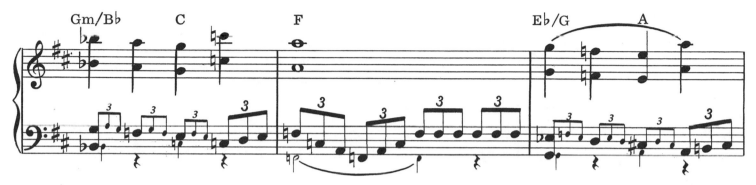

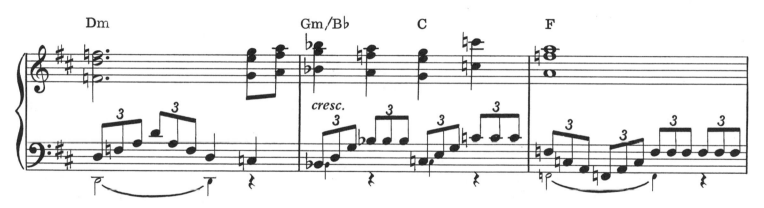

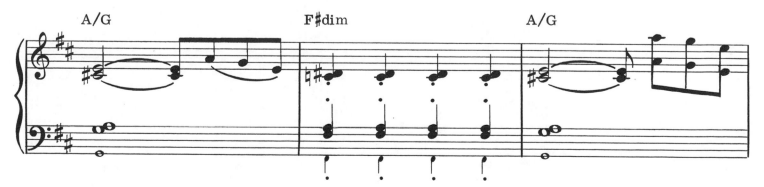

201

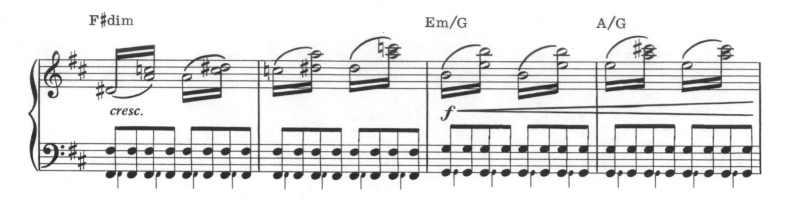

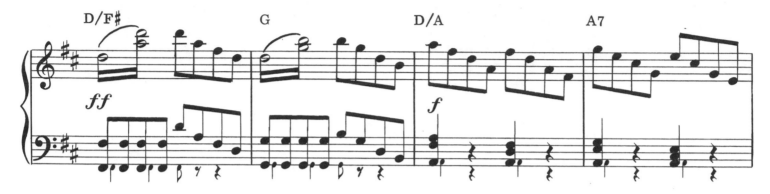

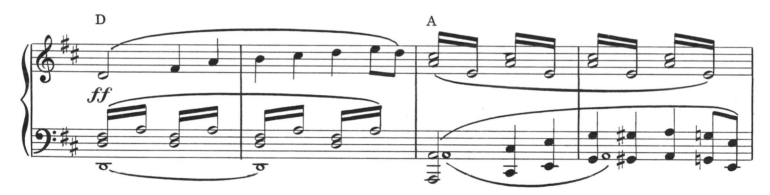

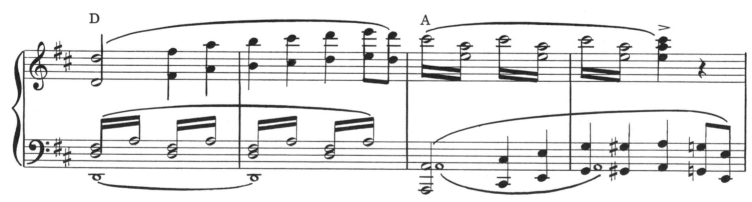

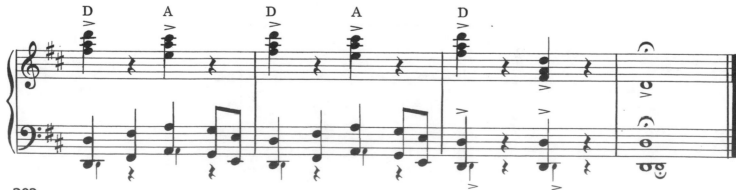

Beethoven: Violin Concerto
Second and Third Movement Themes
Ludwig van Beethoven

It is astonishing to learn that by the time this concerto was introduced (see page 200 for a theme from the first movement), Beethoven was well on the way to losing his hearing completely. However, none of the anguish of his adversity finds its way into the piece: there is only emotional warmth, intensity and structural perfection, as can be heard in the dreamy main theme of the second movement and, at last, the energy and eventual majesty of the finale.

Rondo (with spirit, in 2; ♩.=1 beat)

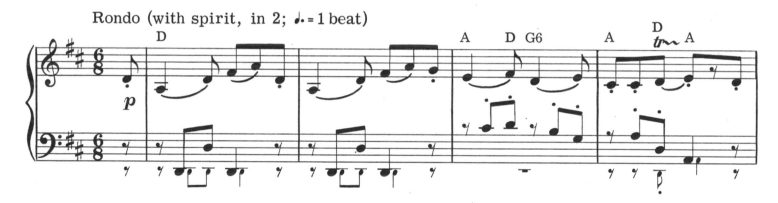

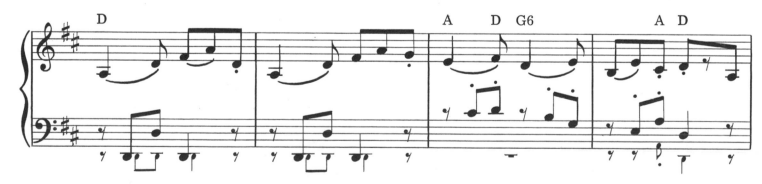

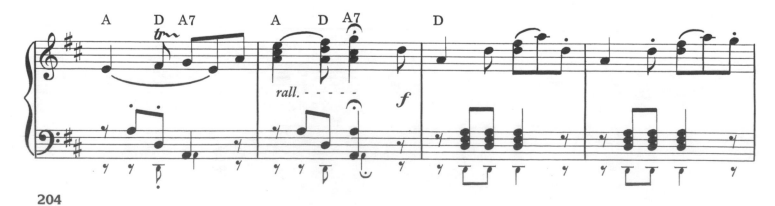

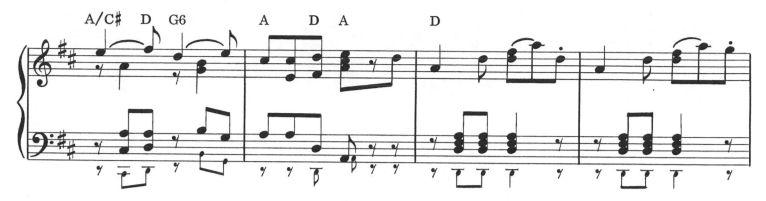

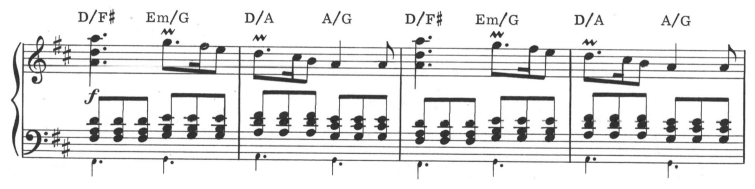

"Archduke" Trio
Third Movement Theme

Ludwig van Beethoven

By 1811, Beethoven had seemingly come to terms with his rapidly encroaching deafness. Though money was short and a series of unsuccessful love affairs had brought moments of deep personal despair, his overall vision seemed to have rallied. His Sixth Symphony, the "Pastoral," was finished and exuded a sunny sense of calm, even flashes of humor. Around this time also, he turned out the famed Trio in B Flat, nicknamed the "Archduke" because he dedicated it to Archduke Rudolph of Austria, one of his piano students. Scored for piano, violin and cello, it gives us glimpses of the kind of introspective turn of mind that was to dominate much of his later work for small ensembles, in particular the later quartets and the last of the piano sonatas. Beethoven would encounter more despair, but for the moment his artistic fertility and his popularity were on the rise. The Trio's sunny third-movement theme, presented here, is characteristic of that sanguine period in the composer's life.

Andante cantabile
(Not fast, but with movement and a singing tone)

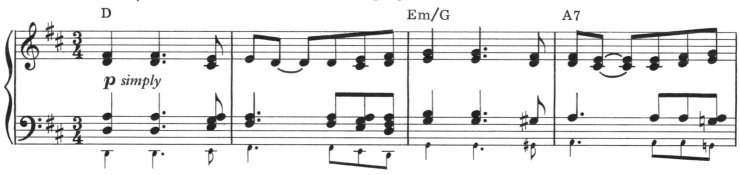

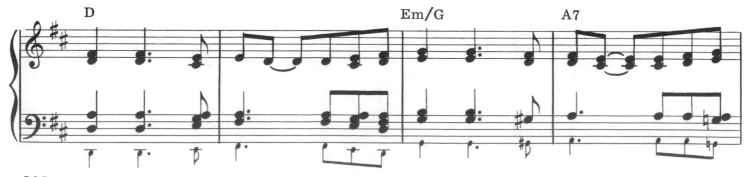

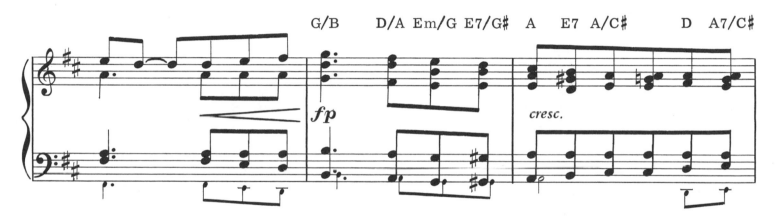

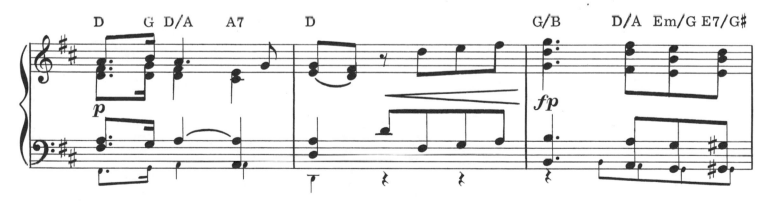

Brahms: Piano Concerto No. 2
Third Movement-Opening Theme

Johannes Brahms

Johannes Brahms' second mighty piano concerto has been proclaimed throughout the years as a "monumental achievement" and the "greatest music ever written for the piano." However, at an early performance in Vienna in 1882, the prominent critic Eduard Hanslick complained that the work was less a concerto than a "symphony with piano obbligato." Another critic objected because, he said, the concerto lacked "brilliance." History, of course, has been Brahms' vindication. The small, portly man with the big cigar and flowing beard, who had spent his youth playing piano in Hamburg bars and brothels, had let 23 years pass before trying a successor to his first piano concerto. Never in a hurry, Brahms had waited until his thoughts were clear and organized, then set his concerto down on paper. Its third movement is one of his most beautiful, opening with a solo cello setting out a melody of transcendental beauty. The piano, when it enters, carries this theme along, then introduces a second theme, equally serene. Another sublime moment comes further on, as twin clarinets elevate their theme above a quiet, thoughtful piano counterline.

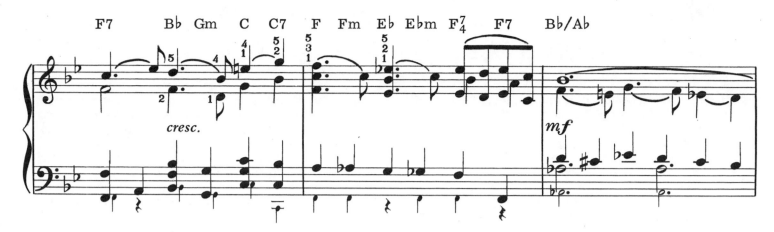

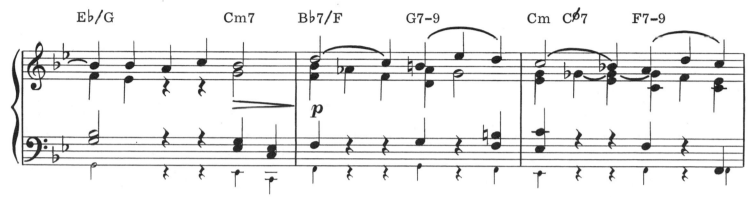

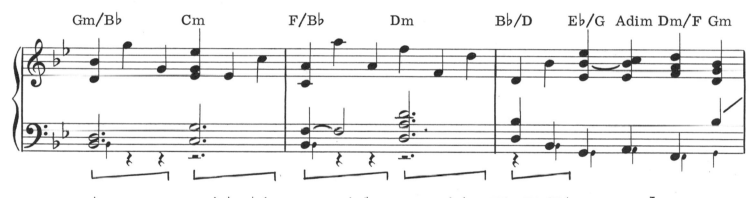

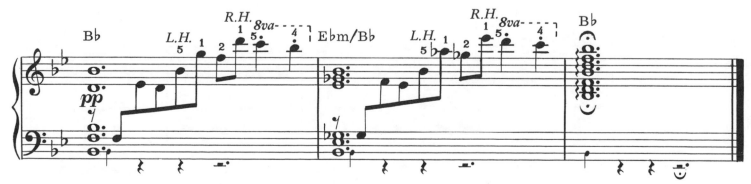

Haydn: Trumpet Concerto in E Flat
Third Movement-Opening Theme

Franz Joseph Haydn

Until inventors in Germany and France patented a system of piston valves in the early 19th century, the trumpet's use was limited. Basically just a curved length of tubing through which a player forced a vibrating stream of air, the trumpet could easily produce only the tones of the basic harmonic series, such as those heard in most military bugle calls. The few composers who took the instrument seriously wrote mostly in the extreme high range, where the notes of the natural series are close together. Then, in the early 1700s, Viennese court trumpeter Anton Weidinger came up with a trumpet that sported a row of keys along its bell, permitting it to produce the notes of the chromatic scale. Franz Joseph Haydn was one of several composers who were quick to see its new potential. His tuneful, elegant Trumpet Concerto in E Flat remains a favorite of the brass repertoire. It uses the middle register of the instrument with particular clarity and affords the player two opportunities to show off creativity and prowess in unaccompanied cadenzas. Many recordings of this third-movement theme have been made, including ones by jazz trumpeters Al Hirt and Wynton Marsalis.

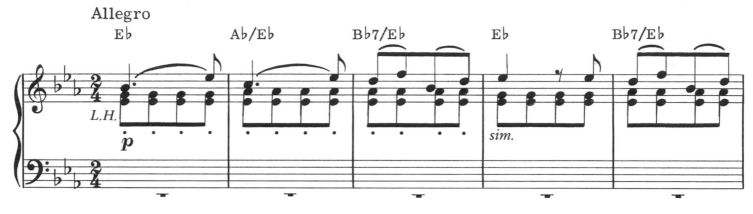

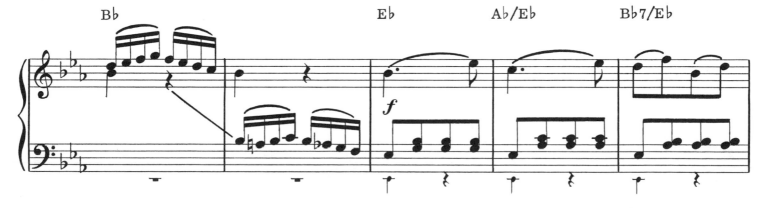

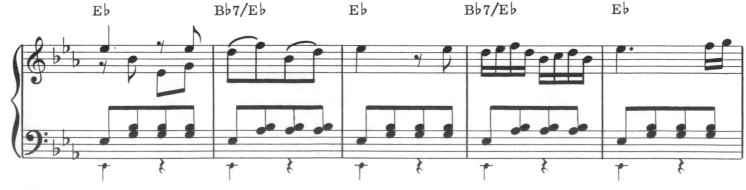

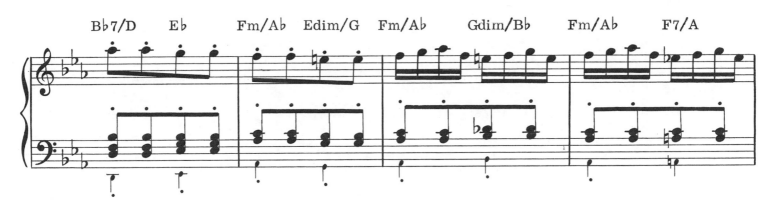

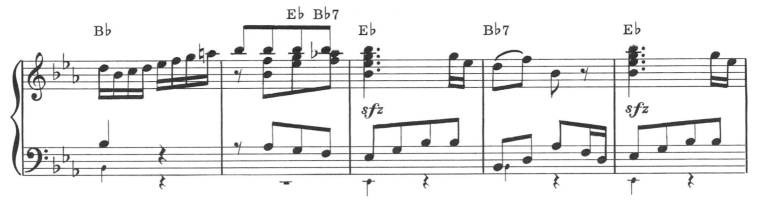

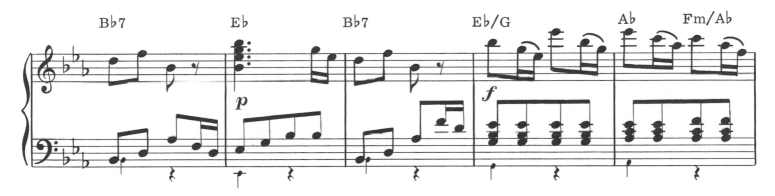

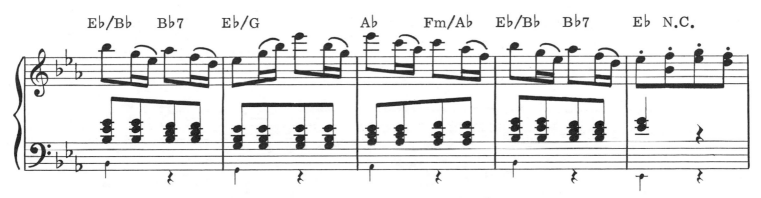

Carnival of the Animals Suite

Camille Saint-Saëns

Camille Saint-Saëns enjoyed great popularity in his lifetime — as a concert pianist, as a composer and as chief organist at the Madeleine, one of the most exalted churches in Paris. And yet he was a man born out of his time, a time when Romanticism, the imperative of pure emotion, inspiration and the grand gesture, came more and more to dominate European cultural thought. But Saint-Saëns was at heart a classicist, a man who valued clarity and exactitude, understatement and subtlety. Certainly his 14-part Carnival of the Animals, as civilized a piece of caricature as exists in all

music, more than illustrates that. (Excerpted here are the selections "Turtles," "Personages with Long Ears," "Elephants" and the "Finale.") Despite his having championed such arch-Romantics as Franz Liszt and Hector Berlioz (this piece even incorporates a melody by Berlioz), Saint-Saëns seemed unwilling to accept Romanticism on its own terms and as a result became something of a cultural throwback, more often venerated than heeded. He, in turn, moved ever further from the lightness of spirit that had made this "grand zoological fantasy" so delightful and gently ironic.

Turtles

*This melody is, of course, from Orpheus in the Underworld by Jacques Offenbach.

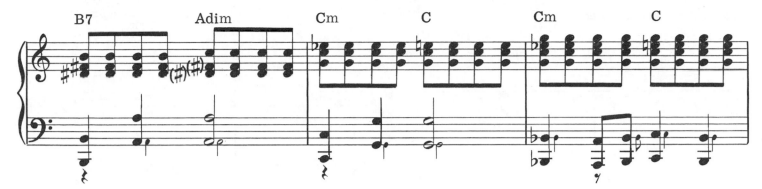

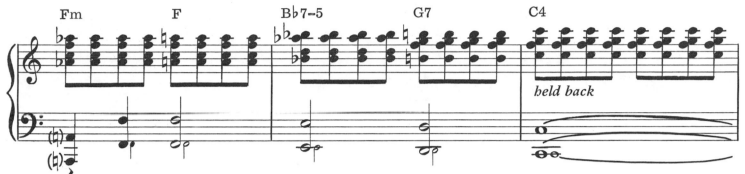

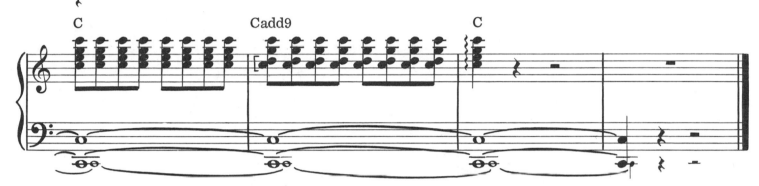

Personages with Long Ears

Ad lib

Elephants

Allegretto pomposo

Bring out the bass

To Coda

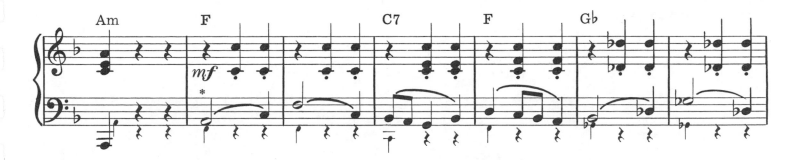

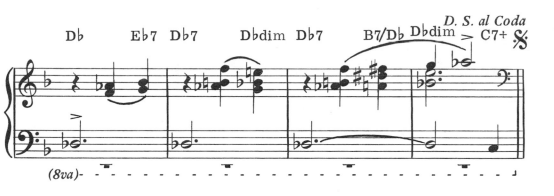

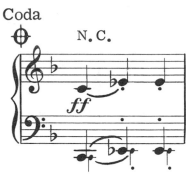

*Melody is from Ballet of the Sylphs by Hector Berlioz.

Finale

With spirit

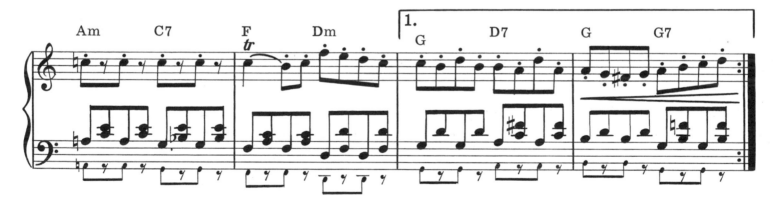

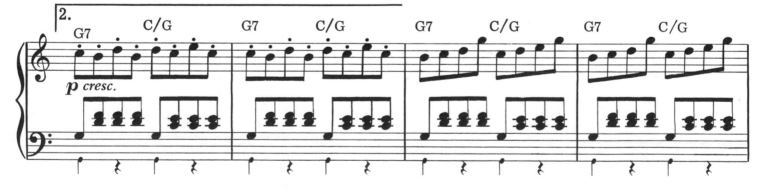

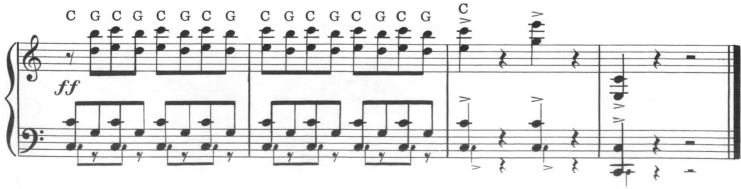

The Sorcerer's Apprentice

(Introduction / Main Theme)

Paul Dukas

It seems ironic that Paul Dukas's vigorous symphonic poem The Sorcerer's Apprentice, written in 1897 and based on a poem by Goethe, should be better known than the composer's name or any of his other works. The reason is Walt Disney's 1940 animated masterpiece Fantasia, which turned the sorcerer's apprentice into a harried Mickey Mouse battling an army of determined brooms. For the composer, it would have been an unexpected — and perhaps not altogether welcome — kind of immortality. Dukas in life had made his mark well: a student at the Paris

Conservatory at 16, he later won respect as a teacher, critic and composer in equal measure. Among his most respected works were an opera, Ariane and Bluebeard, and the short ballet Le Péri, presented in 1912 and all but lost in the furor attending Igor Stravinsky's The Firebird and Petrushka. But there is a mystery in Dukas's later life. While still in his 40s, although he continued to compose, he stopped publishing his compositions, and before he died in 1935, he destroyed more than 20 years' worth of his own music. Why? We will probably never know.

About march tempo (each measure = 1 beat)

Organ: Hold D pedal throughout this page.

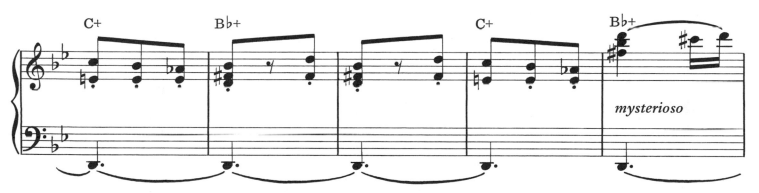

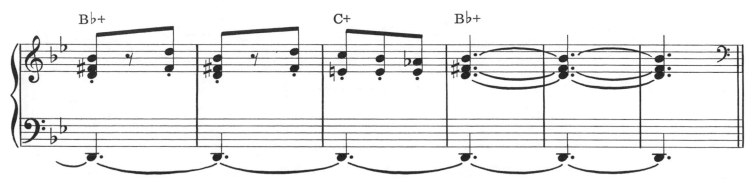

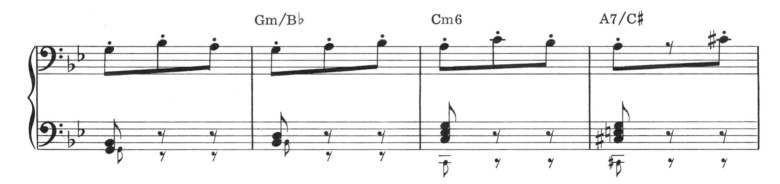

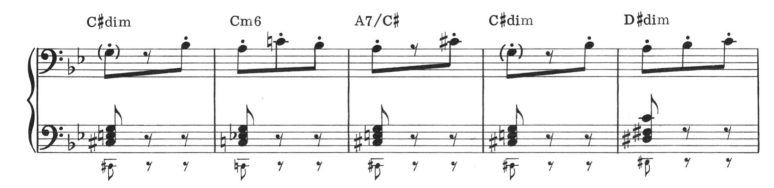

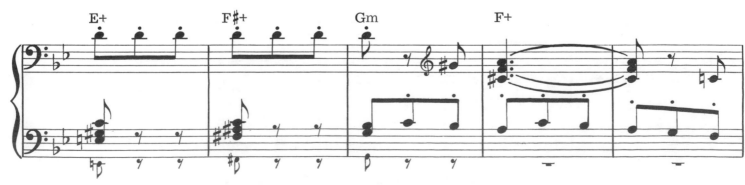

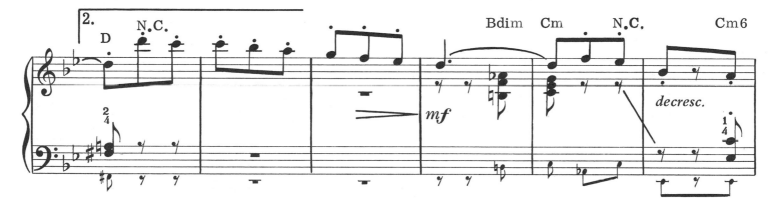

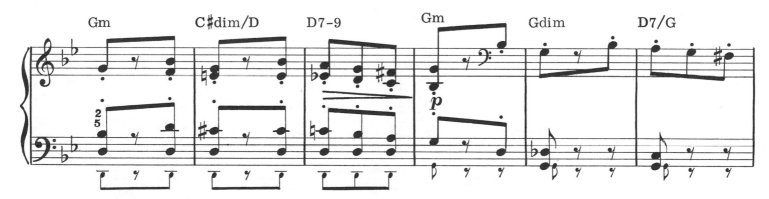

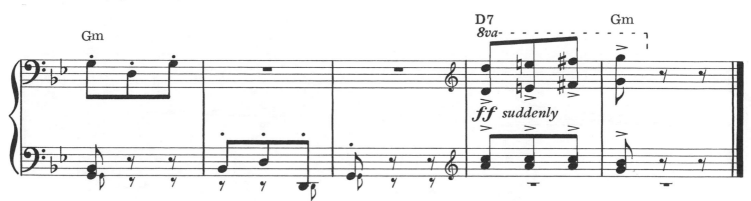

Béla Bartók

Bear Dance

Throughout his life, Béla Bartók insisted that he had spent his happiest years not as an internationally renowned composer shuttling among world capitals but as an ardent, endlessly curious young researcher with an Edison cylinder recording machine. Born into a comfortable Hungarian family, he had studied piano both with private teachers and at the Budapest Academy of Music. But his growing aware-

ness of the Hungarian independence movement and his first meeting with composer Zoltán Kodály triggered deep interest in the folk-music tradition of his own people. Traveling throughout Hungary, Rumania and Slovakia, Bartók recorded peasant instrumentalists and singers on his cumbersome Edison machine. Getting the peasants to perform was sometimes difficult. Many feared that the machine's large horn would swallow their voices forever. The "Bear Dance" is included in his **Sonatina**, a collection of folk tunes from Transylvania in what is now Rumania. Its ponderous, waddling rhythm accurately reflects both its subject and the tunes from which it is drawn.

Moderately, in 2 ($\quad$ =1 beat)

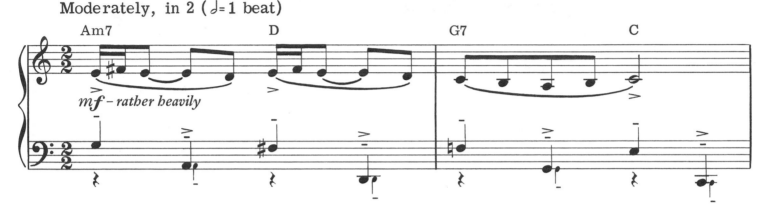

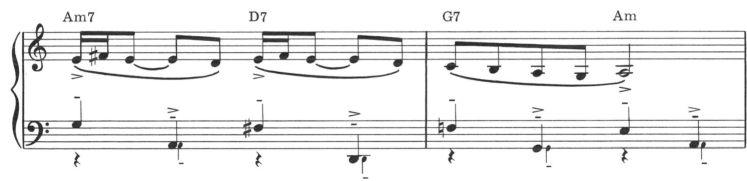

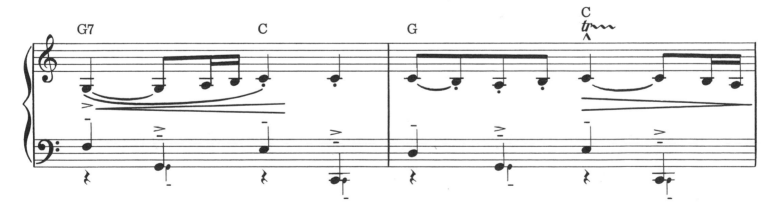

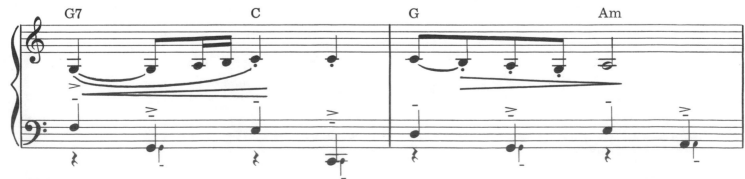

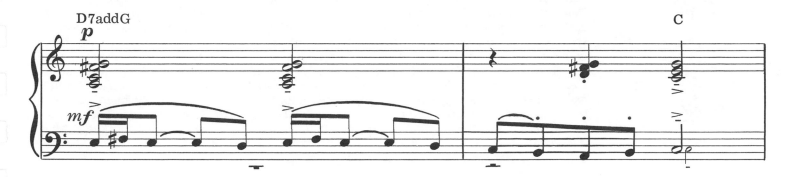

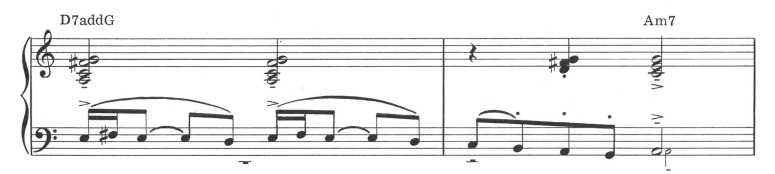

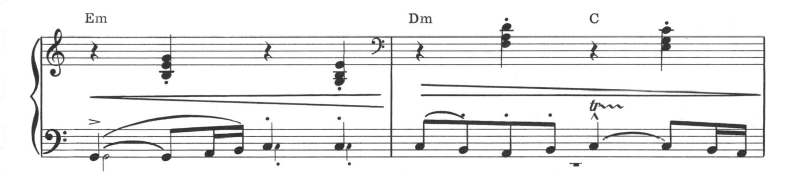

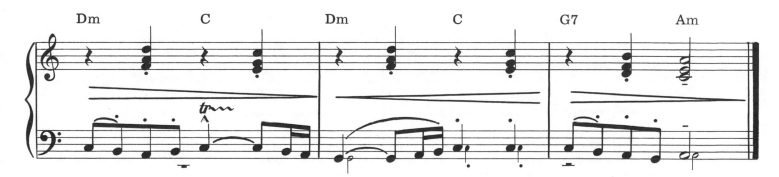

Golliwog's Cake Walk

Claude Debussy

As early as the mid-1800s, astute musical thinkers were calling attention to the black folk tradition of America. Antonín Dvořák, on his visit to the United States in the 1890s, hailed the "beautiful and varied themes" of Negro music and found in them "all that is needed for a great and noble school of music." Yet throughout the early 20th century, European composers seemed more interested in this aspect of America's young culture than did their U.S. counterparts. Ragtime elements and, subsequently, jazz elements appeared in the music of Igor Stravinsky, Erik Satie, Darius Milhaud and in this delightful piece by Claude Debussy. It was one of several miniatures that he wrote for his daughter Claude-Emma, or "Chou-Chou" as he nicknamed her. He composed the pieces, known collectively as The Children's Corner, between 1906 and 1908. In France and Britain, a golliwog is a doll in the form of a caricature of a black child. In Debussy's ragtimey "cake walk" (he probaby knew little about the actual dance called a cake walk, which depends on grace and smooth movement), Chou-Chou's golliwog lurches drunkenly and erratically through its start-and-stop routine.

With spirit

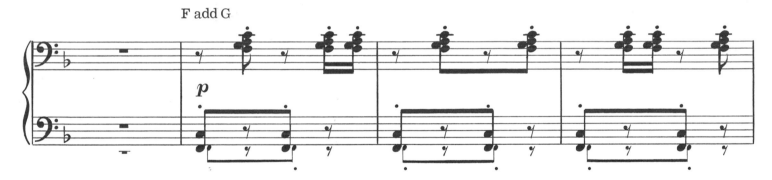

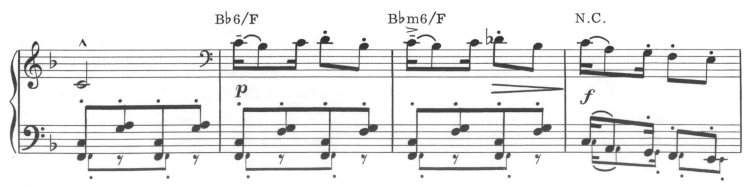

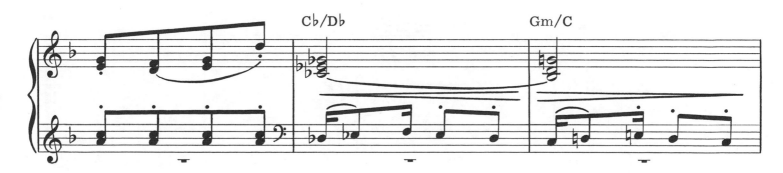

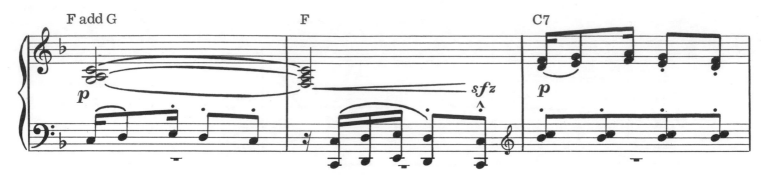

8va lower

Dance of the Comedians

from **The Snow Maiden** Nicolai Rimsky-Korsakov

Nicolai Rimsky-Korsakov was full of surprises. He launched his composing career while still an officer in the Russian Navy and allegedly wrote most of his immensely successful first symphony on shipboard. When his membership in the group of influential young Russian composers called the "Mighty Five" won him a post teaching composition and orchestration at the University of St. Petersburg — a job he was unqualified to fill — he kept one step ahead of his students by pursuing a nighttime crash course in the very subject he was teaching by day. His opera The Snow Maiden was surprising in a different way. It was based on an imaginative fairy tale by the dramatist Alexander Ostrovsky, and the result delighted even Ostrovsky. The playwright wrote appreciatively that he "could never have imagined anything more appropriate to the subject and expressing with such vitality all the poetry both of the Russian pagan cult and of the heroine of the tale — the girl whose heart is at first as cold as snow but later is filled with unrestrained passion." The exuberant "Dance of the Comedians" begins Act III and presages the moment when the shepherd Lehl dances with the Snow Maiden Snegurouchka, then forsakes her for another girl — with cataclysmic results.

Quickly, with spirit

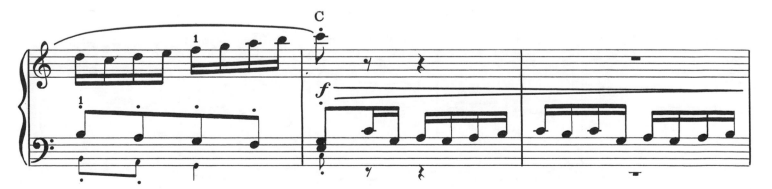

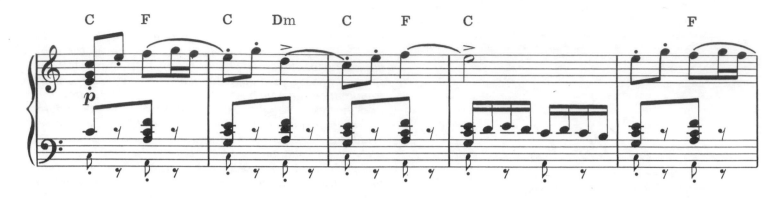

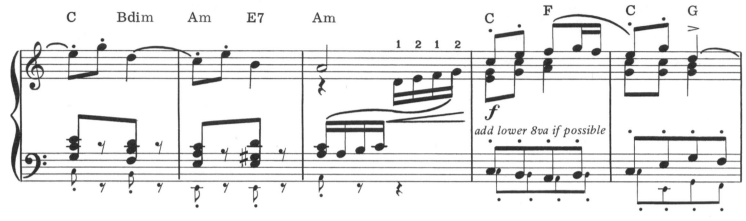

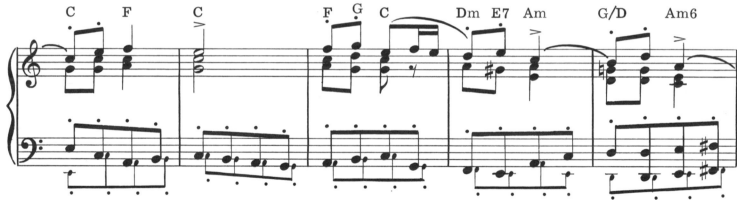

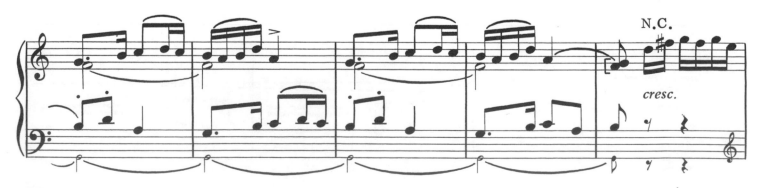

8va lower- -

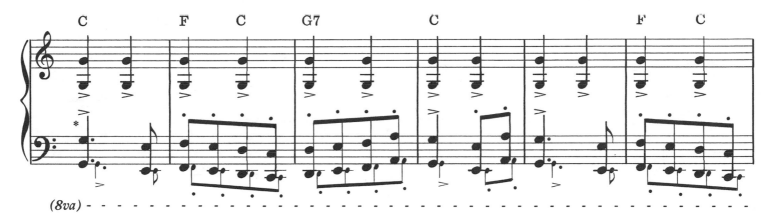

(8va) -

(8va)- - - - - - - - - - - - - -⌐   as is

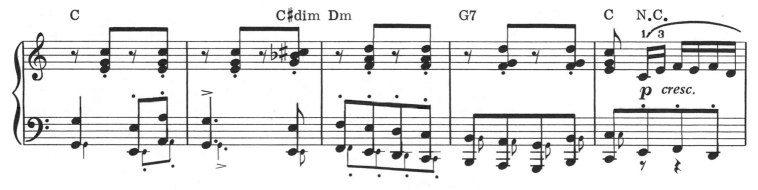

Performance note—Pianists: exaggerate the bass line; organists: consider the possibility of making this a pedal solo.

Petrushka Mini-Suite

Igor Stravinsky

Throughout a long and productive life, Igor Stravinsky wrote in many idioms, producing masterpieces in all. His one-act ballet Petrushka (1911) is a midway point between the glitter of The Firebird (1910) and the more fully realized achievement of The Rite of Spring (1913). Like them, Petrushka is a blend of realism and illusion, and the allegorical possibilities in the small Punch-and-Judy-style drama taking place among the magician's three dolls — the clown Petrushka, the Moor and the ballerina they both love — are limitless. This "Mini-Suite" (which includes "The Organ Grinder and the Dancer," "The Music Box" and "Russian Dance") blends various themes that run throughout the street scene where the story unfolds — the public square of St. Petersburg.

The Organ Grinder and the Dancer

The Music Box

segue (go directly to the next section)

Russian Dance

Brightly (about march tempo)

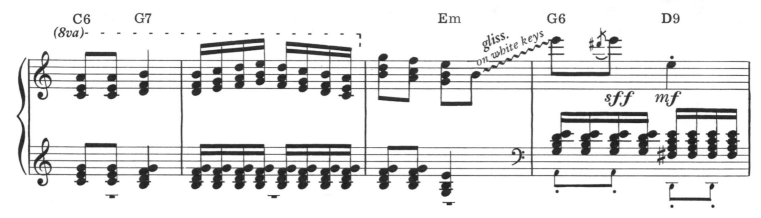

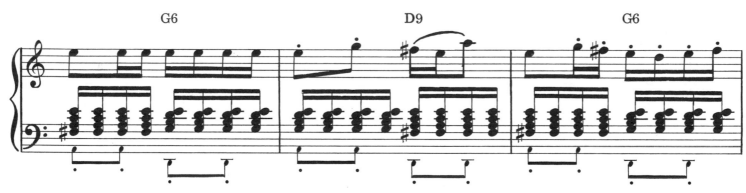

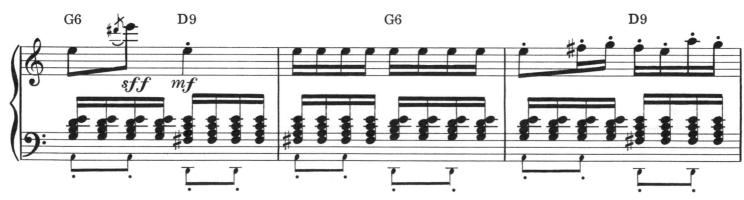

NOTE: The "Russian Dance" is much easier than it may appear. The fast chordal passages can be played with the right hand in a locked position on the white keys.

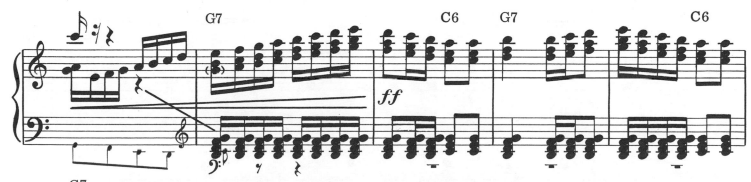

Classical Symphony - Gavotte

Sergei Prokofiev

In one important respect, the first symphony of Sergei Prokofiev, which gave us this Gavotte, remains an anomaly. Why did a young composer whose works abound in wit, energy, clashing dissonance and a spirit of mischief choose to write a brief orchestral piece of such clarity and elegant classicism? An easy answer lies in Prokofiev's respect for classical form. For all the controversy surrounding the dissonant textures of such landmarks as his Second Piano Concerto, he remained ever fascinated with the purity of 18th-century classicism. "I strive for simplicity and more melody," he once wrote. "Of course, I have used dissonance, but there has been too much dissonance. . . . We need a simpler, more tuneful sort of music." Indeed, had the Classical Symphony been all he wrote, Prokofiev's utterance would have occasioned no bewilderment. But anyone who has heard his opera The Love of Three Oranges or his ballet Romeo and Juliet or his score for the film Alexander Nevsky must wonder at the apparent contradictions.

Sergei Prokofiev

Not too fast

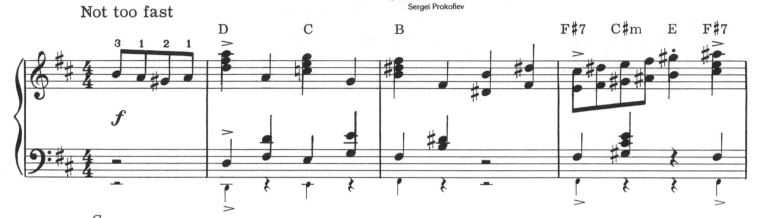

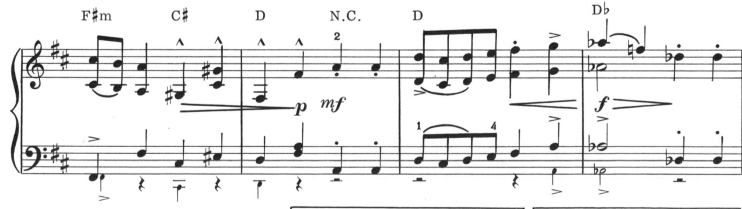

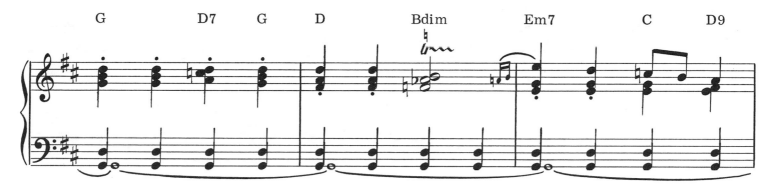

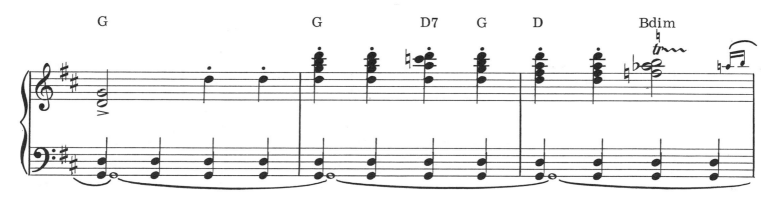

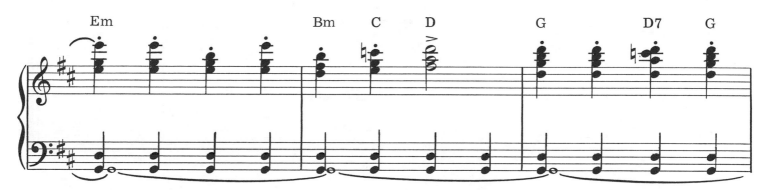

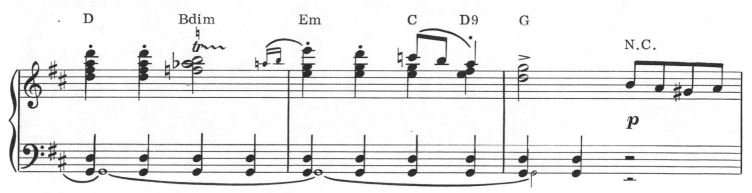

This entire section over a G-D pastoral pedal point.

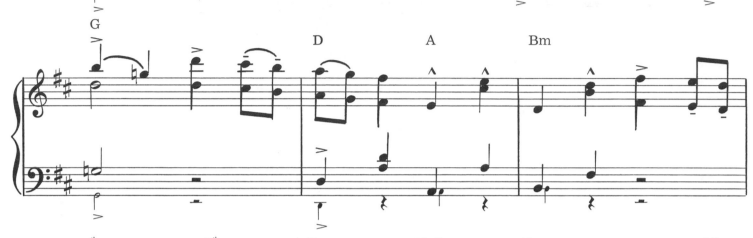

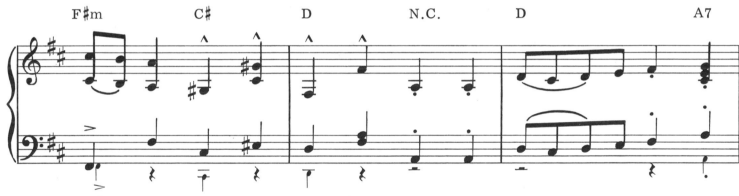

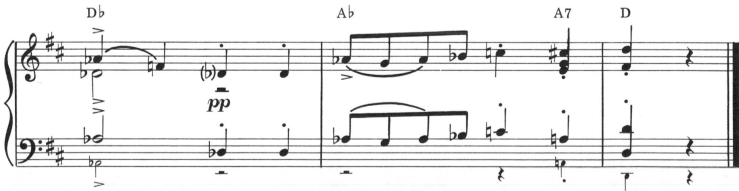

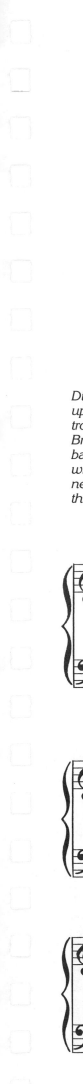

10
Popular Masterpieces in March Time

Colonel Bogey

Kenneth J. Alford

Did a Colonel Bogey ever really exist? Was he some stiff-upper-lip officer who commanded a garrison of British troops somewhere in the Punjab during the last days of the British Empire? No one knows — and the British military bandmaster Frederick J. Ricketts, who as Kenneth J. Alford wrote this and other stirring marches in the early 1900s, never let on. "Colonel Bogey" might, in fact, have remained the exclusive province of Her Majesty's Armed Forces had it not been for the 1957 David Lean film The Bridge on the River Kwai. *In it, the music seems to reflect the indomitable spirit of a World War II British Army unit keeping their heads high even while suffering hardship at the hands of their Japanese captors. For those who have seen the film, the free-stepping gait and simple melody of "Colonel Bogey" will always evoke the figure of Alec Guinness standing tall before his men, instilling in them the spirit to carry on despite the odds.*

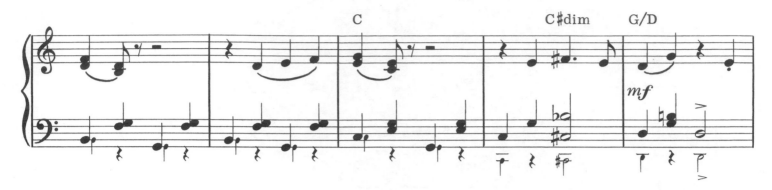

2nd time, play an 8va higher till final ending

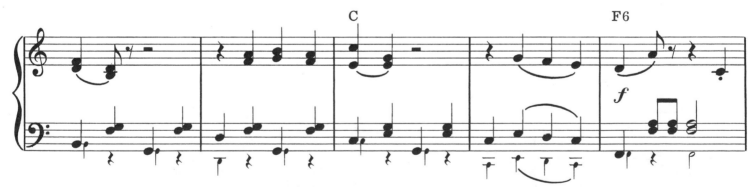

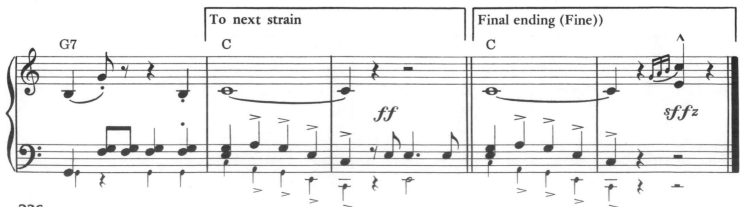

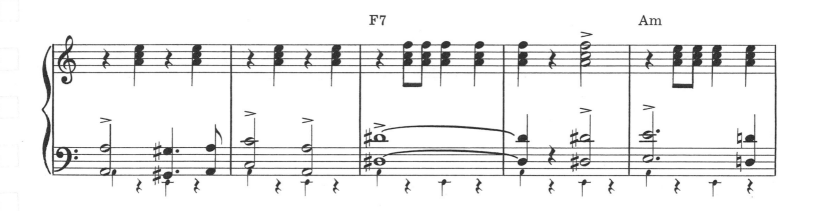

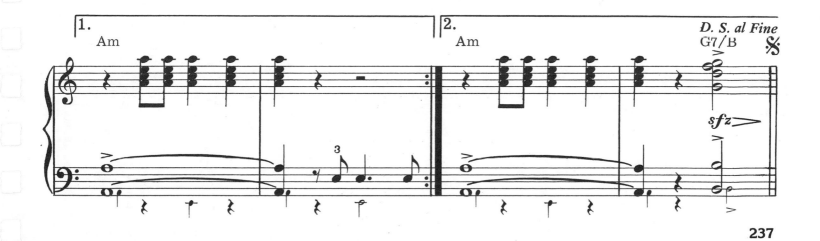

Soldiers' Chorus from Faust

Charles Gounod

Though Charles Gounod studied for the priesthood in his late 20s, he was known throughout his life as a compulsive womanizer. And, indeed, this curious juxtaposition of sacred and profane, of exaltation and bathos, is a strand that runs through his life and work. His early operas, for example, are sentimental, melodramatic extravaganzas in the overblown style of Giacomo Meyerbeer, but when he moved from the Paris Opera to the more creative atmosphere of that city's Théâtre-Lyrique, he turned out five operas that are by common consent his finest work. Chief among these was

his adaptation of the legend of Faust, as set out by Goethe. The result, first staged in 1859, hardly approaches the German poet's metaphysical austerity; it instead concentrates on the romance between Faust — the learned doctor who sells his soul to the devil in exchange for youth, knowledge and magical powers — and the heroine, Marguerite. The stirring "Soldiers' Chorus" occurs in Act IV, as a group of foot soldiers, Marguerite's brother Valentine among them, return from battle. It is a prelude to tragedy, as Faust soon after kills the youth in a duel.

Moderately slow march, in 2 (♩. = 1 beat)

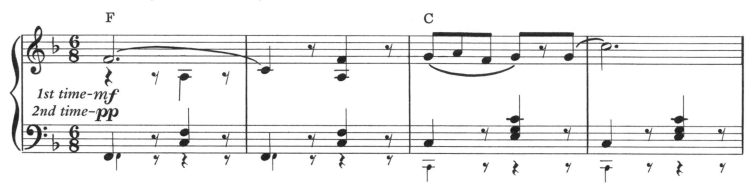

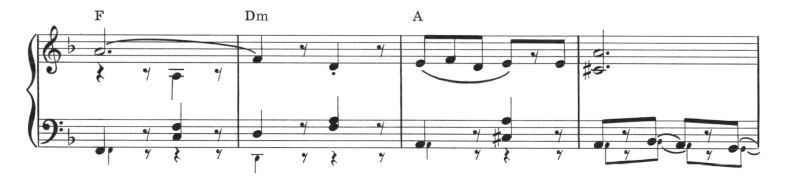

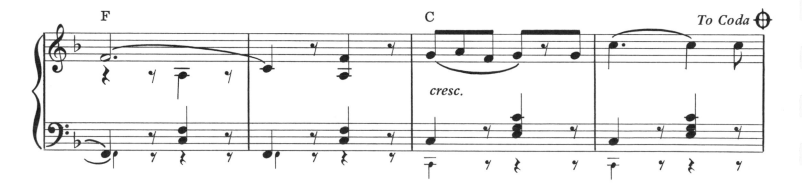

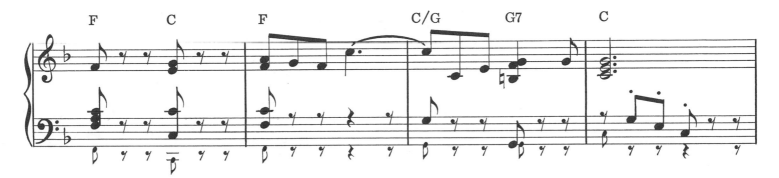

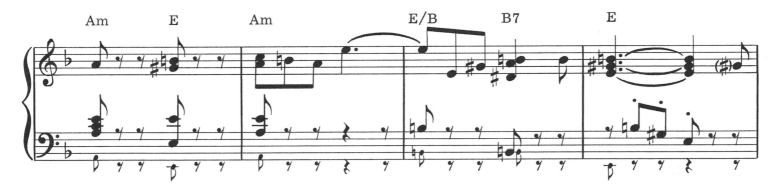

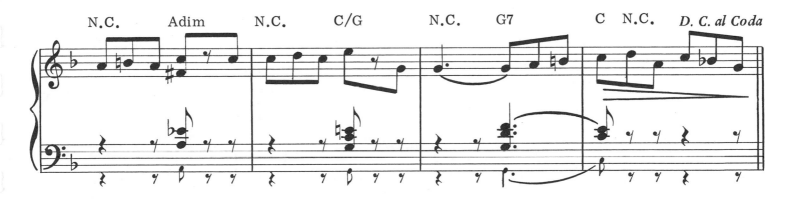

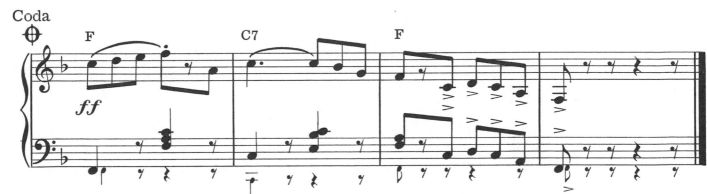

ENTRANCE OF THE GLADIATORS
(Thunder and Blazes)
Julius Fučík

Probably without realizing it, every child (or grownup) who has been to the circus and thrilled to the strains of the vigorous march known as "Thunder and Blazes" has been listening to the music of a 19th-century Austrian Army bandmaster named Julius Fučík. Fučík called the march "Entrance of the Gladiators," and it is one of 240 light works he turned out during his military career. Born in Bohemia (now Czechoslovakia), he had envisioned a career spent writing symphonies and other ambitious pieces. But fate decreed otherwise, and he found his fame — and considerable financial success — as a composer of marches, dances and similar light works. Glory was to come to him not in the concert hall but under the Big Top instead.

March tempo

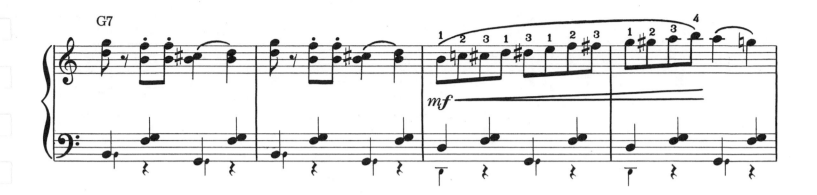

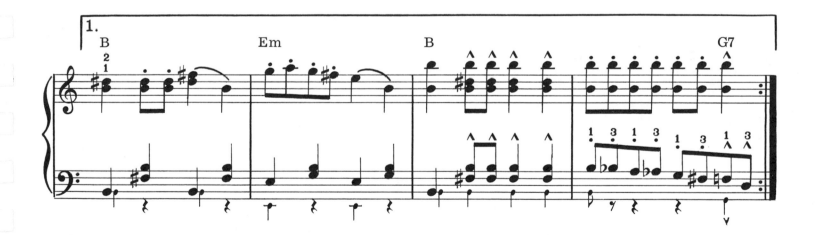

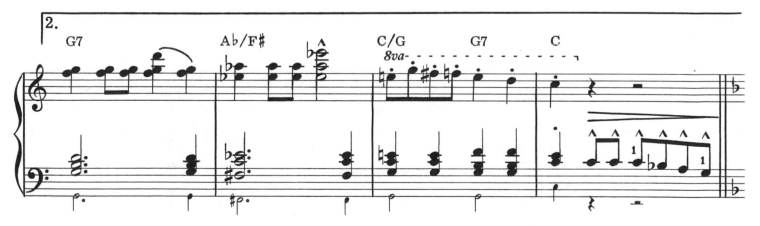

Trio

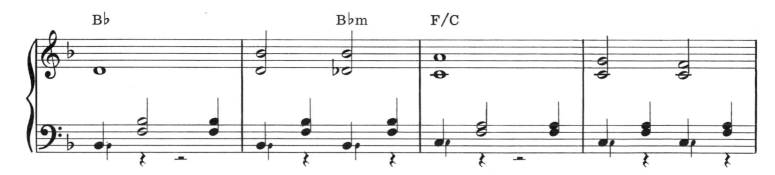

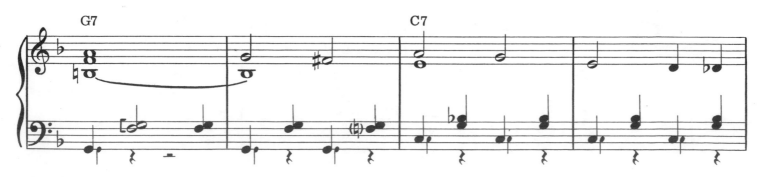

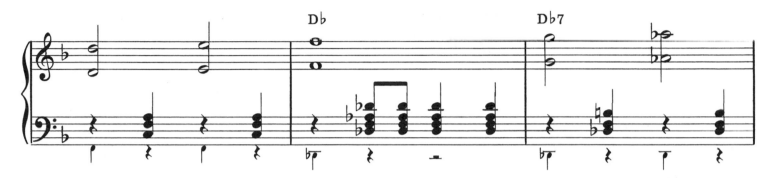

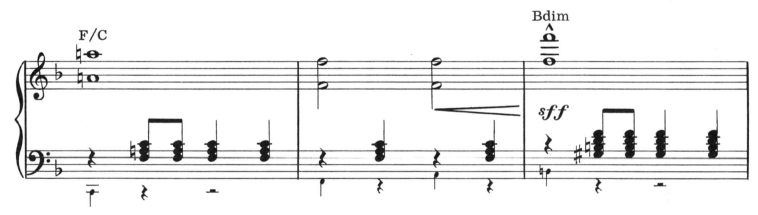

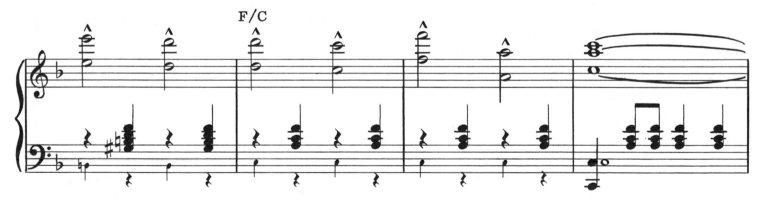

The March of Time

Harold Arlen

Harold Arlen was already well established as a songwriter in 1935 when Time magazine approached him for permission to use a song he had written for an edition of Earl Carroll Vanities on Broadway five years earlier. He had called it "The March of Time" — which also happened to be the title of a new radio series that Time planned to launch. What was needed was a theme serious enough to complement the commanding voice of announcer Westbrook Van Voorhis. Arlen agreed and for the next two years received a weekly check of $125 from Time, Inc. The series was a success — so much so that the next step appeared to be a March of Time movie. More checks? No. Someone on the production end of the film discovered that with a few note changes here and there the theme music could be copyrighted as a new melody — meaning that the payments to Arlen could cease. After some thought, the composer decided not to sue. The checks had been "found money," and Arlen and his partner, lyricist Ted Koehler, were doing well enough with such hits as "Between the Devil and the Deep Blue Sea" and "Stormy Weather" not to even notice.

Moderate march tempo, in 2 (♩. = 1 beat)

Introduction

1st strain (Verse)

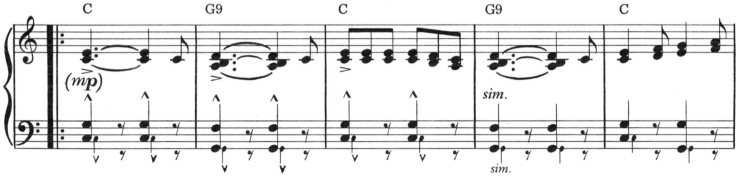

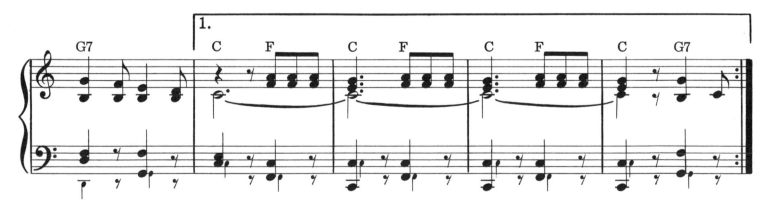

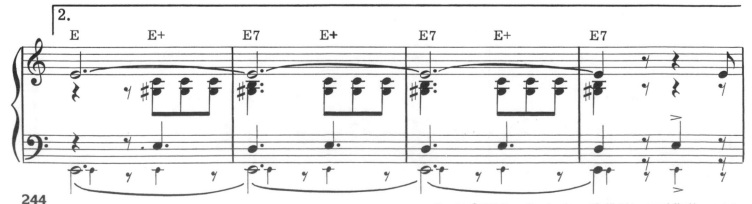

244

2nd strain (Chorus)

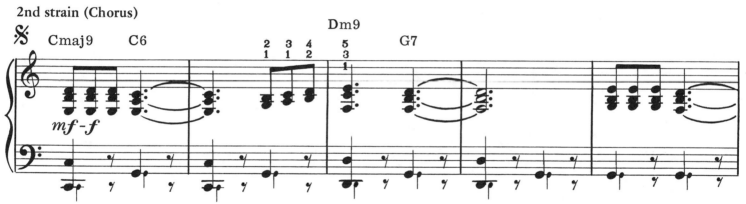

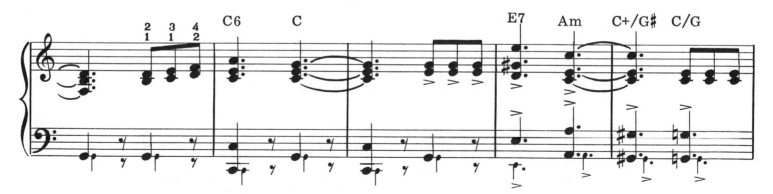

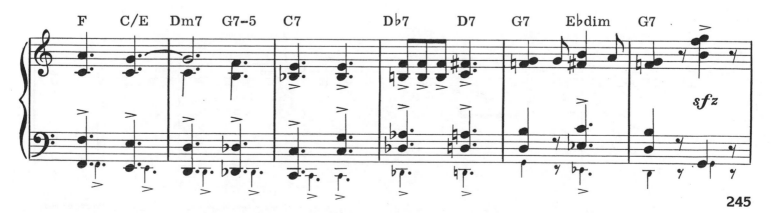

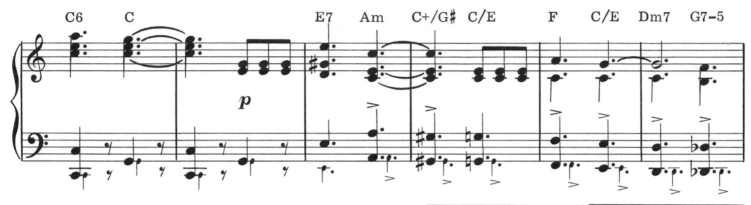

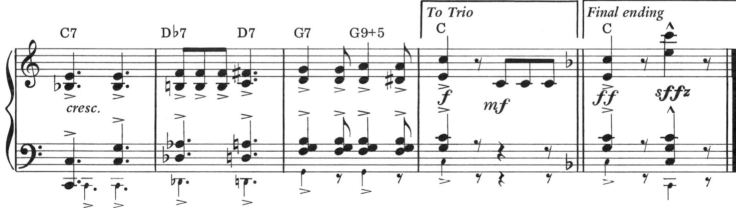

3rd strain

Trio

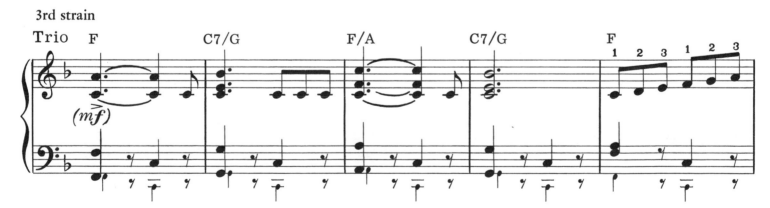

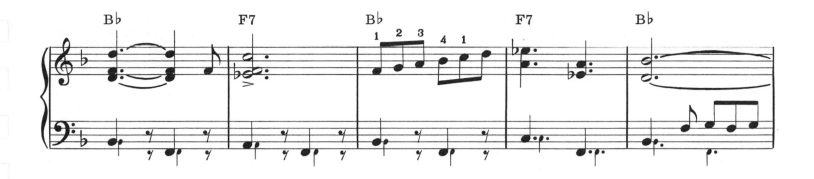

gradually gaining in strength and intensity

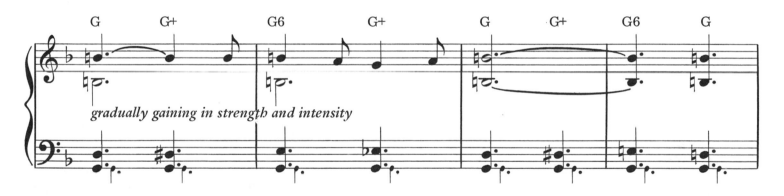

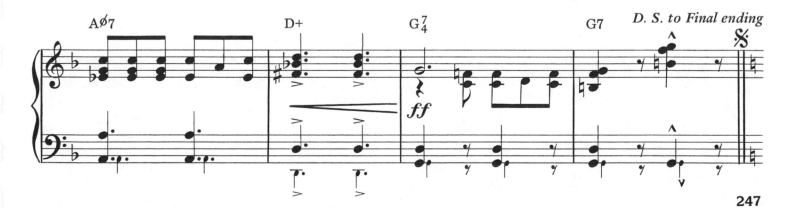

Washington Post March

John Philip Sousa

This eternally popular 6/8 march proved fateful for its composer, "March King" John Philip Sousa. He wrote it on commission in 1889, while leading the U.S. Marine Band. The occasion was a ceremony in which the Washington Post, the newspaper of the march title, presented prizes in an essay contest it had sponsored to "stimulate the urge of self-expression among children." Sousa sold his rights to the composition for $35 — then watched as the tune grew to become an immensely popular staple of the marching-band repertoire. Perhaps because of such experiences, Sousa later became a charter member of the newly formed American

Society of Composers, Authors and Publishers (ASCAP). In the words of the ASCAP Biographical Dictionary, the organization's aim is "to make it possible for creators of music to be paid for performances of their compositions." Throughout his life, Sousa remained a creative and prolific force, and not only in music. Less known than either his marches or operas (El Capitan, The Free Lance and The American Maid) is his activity as a writer of several novels, numerous magazine and newspaper articles, and a most readable autobiography, Marching Along. In all, an extremely diverse and fascinating man.

Brisk march tempo (♩. = 1 beat)

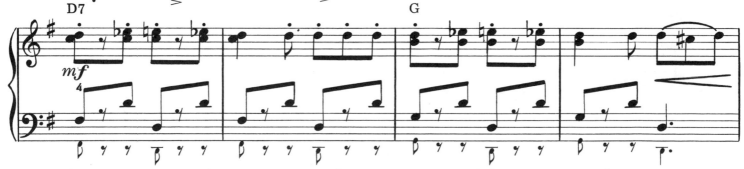

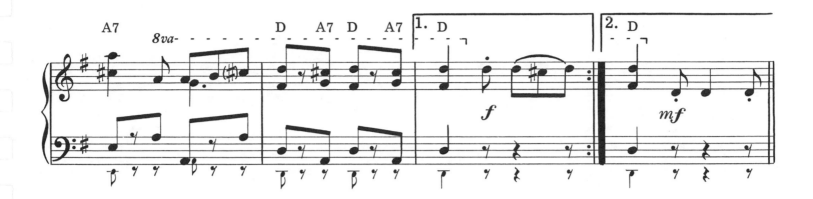

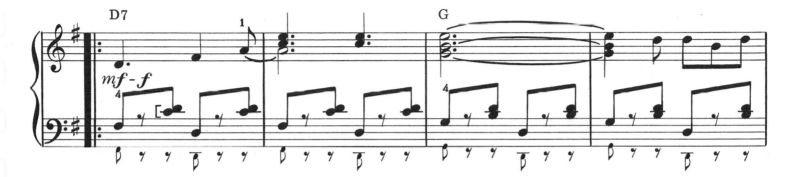

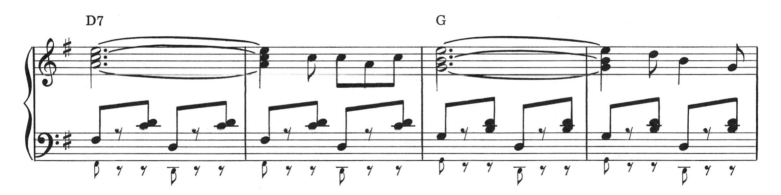

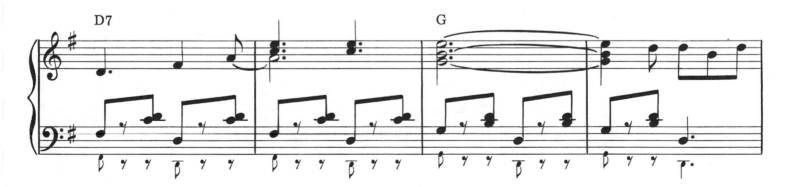

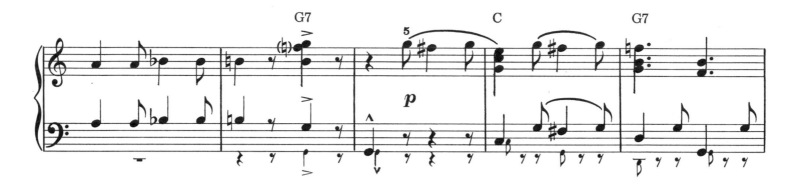

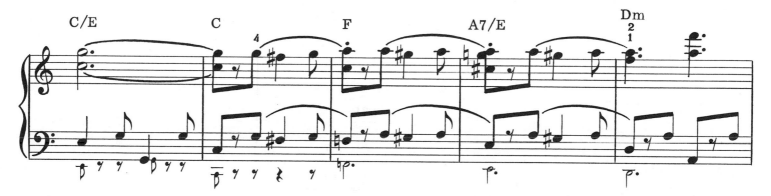

Index to the Composers and Their Works